Eat, Sleep, and Breathe!

With Joy,

Sue Stults

Psalm 121

2018

Praise for Sue Stults, *Reaching Beyond the Rail*, and her previous book *The Personal Health Care Manual*

"Sue's calling to the caregiving ministry was a godsend to us as we were suddenly confronted with end-of-life issues for our two mothers (one month apart), and another elderly relative with Alzheimer's. Her practical suggestions, personal attention, and advice were invaluable. We used *The Personal Health Care Manual* constantly to keep ourselves current and organized. We frequently referred to information gleaned at the Caregiver's Conference she organized. Outstanding help!"

— Barbara Syring, Caregiver's Conference Attendee

"Sue is the epitome of a compassionate and caring person. All her caring has led her to helping so many people. The Care Conferences she puts on and her *The Personal Health Care Manual* were excellent resources for me to put together for my husband. Now, since my own stem cell transplant, I take my manual with me even to The Mayo Clinic for my annual follow-up appointments. Thank you, Sue, for leading me with gentleness, and showing me how to lead with *respect, honor, and dignity*."

— Ranee Palacios, Realtor, Broker

"In the many years I have worked with Sue Stults in her business, Compelled by Compassion, Inc., I have developed great respect for her integrity, knowledge, and compassion for others. Sue's book and manual are vital to all ages, not just the elderly."

— Gayle (Woodbury) Lee, Executive Assistant,
Administrator, Compelled by Compassion, Inc.

"Sue has done an amazing job of organizing and pulling resources together so you are in better shape in that moment of need than you would otherwise be."

— Teepa Snow, MS, OTR/L, FAOTA, Nationally Recognized
Dementia Care Consultant and Expert

"Talk with Sue Stults about health care. Learn how her system can work for you to get the quality treatment you and your parents deserve."

— Terry Gargus, MS

"Thank you abundantly, Sue, for your Care Conference and transparency. It was an indispensable seminar. Surely it changed our frame of reference in regard to the elderly and *The Personal Health Care Manual* gave us such a head start!"

— Teena Jones, Caregiver's Conference Attendee

"Sue's presentation on hospice services and her description of the emotions that come with caring for a parent on hospice care were very informative and comforting. I appreciated Sue for saying: 'As caregivers we need to take care of ourselves also, without guilt,' and that it is okay to ask for help. This was a great reference when I found myself in crisis and unable even to think, let alone figure out where to start on my new journey. Everyone should have this reference at home because we all know someone we can help by passing on information gained by this book."

— Mary Fish, Caregivers Conference Attendee

"My husband and I attended Sue's seminar and were pleased that we went and received all the useful information. At times it was pretty funny, which made it enjoyable as well as informative. The information could not have come at a better time as we were coping with the death of our son."

— Joy and Chuck Eastman, Lynnwood, Washington

"In the ten years I've had the honor to know and work with Sue, I have been amazed by her genuine love and care for the hurting. Sue is constantly touching and caring for families during some of their biggest struggles in life. She is an invaluable asset, one that every church should be blessed to have on its team. Our pastoral team at Shoreline Community Church considers itself extremely blessed to have Sue lead our Care Team, direct our Care Conferences, and bless our church community in a multitude of ways."

— Pastor Steve Forrey, Executive Pastor,
Shoreline Community Church

"Sue Stults is one of the hardest workers and most compassionate people I know. You can always count on her to give 150 percent. Her life experiences with the passing of both of her parents has helped shape her into the strong and understanding advocate she is today."

— Shirley Eggebraaten, Former Women's Ministry Director

"I used *The Personal Health Care Manual* prior to my husband's elective heart surgery. Having his affairs in order before his surgery was very important to us. I can see the manual being used at any age prior to surgery. Sue is helpful, insightful, and tenderhearted. I accompanied her on a visit with an elderly church member and observed as she ministered to her and her adult son. She imparted helpful information and wisdom. Sue exemplifies professionalism and performs with tenderness, kindness, and love. She is honest and genuine...always."

— Janice Smith, Fellow Care Team Member

"The information we received from Sue Stults helped my sister and me every step of the way with our mom. From caregiving to hospice to grieving afterwards, Sue was a huge help."

— Carole Gilbreath, Lake Forest Park, Washington

"We had an immediate connection with Sue because we could feel her passionate desire to come alongside people as they walk in the deep valleys of illness and grief. She is an encourager, knowing when to speak, and when just to listen. Her ability to make friendly the foreign world of medicine has been a God-given gift to us. She stood with us, providing comfort during the entire day of my husband's life-threatening surgery. Sue is the kind of person you pray will be with you in your time of need. We are so thankful God brought Sue into our lives."

— Linda and Jerry Watkins, Mountlake Terrace, Washington

"I called Sue because I knew she had the answers."

— Nancy Stainer, Brier, Washington

"As a pastor, friend, chaplain, and colleague, Sue has earned her knowledge through the School of Life. She has passed the test of time and challenges, both personally and professionally, helping people wrestle with end-of-life issues and challenges time and time again. Her work is unique, desperately needed, and a breath of fresh air for individuals and families trying to navigate the end-of-life terrain."

— Pastor Gary Chupik, Professional Chaplain of the Seattle Thunderbirds and Founder of Intelligent Design Leadership

"Sue Stults is an extraordinary woman. I was her pastor for ten years, and during that time, I selected her to be the head of our Care Ministry. She assisted me in (and initiated) a wide variety of care needs, including area-wide seminars she developed that have attracted hundreds of people on several occasions. There is a huge need for all adult children to know how to care for Mom and Dad in their later years. Sue has helped us frame the help needed with great care and wisdom. She is a woman of high integrity and extraordinary compassion. She is the real deal. I highly recommend her, her book, and any other assistance she has to offer. Well done, good and faithful Sue."

— Bob Stone, Former Lead Pastor, Shoreline Community Church

"Sue is an exceptional speaker with a profound depth of compassion. I loved listening to her."

— Sue Byers, Seattle, Washington

"Having everything in one place and in an organized format helped to reduce my stress throughout the journey with my mom. I have recommended *The Personal Health Care Manual* to friends as their parents begin their journey with their own health issues. I will again be using the manual as I prepare to take care of my aging aunt and uncle. It brings a sense of peace, not chaos, as you navigate through so many different health issues."

— Becky Zornes, Kenmore, Washington

"In my thirty-one years of practice, I have never seen such a great compilation of information for the personal health care advocate. *The Personal Health Care Manual* is an organized, concise, useful tool that is a "must have" for the elderly and their guardians. The last decades of life can be confusing and very complicated. This manual will help all those involved in smoothing out the rough times ahead."

— Dr. Michael D. Kaufman

"I have known Sue for several years, but working with her in caregiving ministry brought me to a new dimension—the needs and concerns of senior adult living. Her compassion and gentle spirit helped me through the new challenges of caring for my senior parents, especially during my father's last days. I am forever grateful and more prepared with knowledge, skills, compassion, and caregiving."

— Vicky Blair, Mountlake Terrace, Washington

"Sue has brought together information and teachings that carry through not just for the children of elderly parents but provide groundwork for those children to incorporate into their own retirement and family estate planning. Sue takes what can be overwhelming elder care and dementia issues and provides concrete educational tools to manage many of those daily challenges and caregiving situations. She relays resources, information, and her own life-learned lessons to others while providing a grounded and practical manner laced with humor and compassion."

— Robert Blair, Former President of the Board, Shoreline Community Church

"*Reaching Beyond the Rail* is a powerful, useful, and educational read. As a licensed mental health counselor, I can offer my clients the useful tools provided in this book. A smart, savvy, and direct 'must read' for all who have aging parents."

— Nancy E. Lewis, LMHC

"As a professional firefighter of forty-two years, I cannot commend the help Sue offers highly enough. The practical tips she provides regarding being prepared ahead of time for emergency situations involving loved ones in your life would have been hugely helpful—and even lifesaving in some instances—if they had been in place during the literally thousands of emergency medical situations I responded to during my career."

— Don Peterson, Retired Lieutenant, Seattle Fire Department

"In August 2009, my ninety-one-year-old mother lay dying in her bed in the middle of the living room.... I spoke with Sue on the phone and began to cry and pour my heart out to her about the emotional roller coaster we were on. She listened very carefully and began to share some amazing wisdom and spiritual advice. She was instrumental in helping me through the loss of my mother, and my father, five years later. Sue is an amazing, compassionate, and caring woman of God, with a wonderful gift of ministering to families experiencing the loss of a loved one."

— Rebeca Collello, Lynnwood, Washington

"By attending one of Sue's lectures on dementia, I gained more understanding of the disease and where my mother was coming from. I also gained some new skillsets on how to interact with her and handle some of her challenges better."

— Kathy Adams, Shoreline, Washington

"I found Sue's four-week class on dementia very helpful. It allowed me to filter everything through the eyes of my situation with my parents. It reaffirmed some things and gave me new insight about others."

— Pam Slothaug, Community Service Chaplain

"I found Sue's presentation on dementia and advocacy very useful, especially on how to respond and handle a loved one with dementia."

— Ted Barrett, Texas

"Great presentation on dementia! Sue kept the focus on the individual. (It's not the person; it's the disease.) I found it informational, but still personal."

— Josiah Belveal, Texas

"Sue Stults has been a banking client of mine for at least ten years. Over the years, we have shared many things we have in common, including aging parents. Her first book, *The Personal Health Care Manual*, is such a useful tool while encouraging empathy of the patients' need for dignity through the end-of-life process. As Sue explains, there are so many things that should be in place early on in the process for the elderly. The manual is an indispensable tool to all caretakers."

— Nancy Engel, VP/Branch Manager, Ballard, Washington

"Both my wife and I attended Sue's Care Conference two years in a row and found the information extremely valuable, especially when my wife's mother began to have a series of medical problems that ended with her death at age ninety-nine. Her hospital stays, multiple medical appointments, changing medications, and care needs required active monitoring by my wife, and the information Sue shared from her experiences were invaluable!"

— Dr. Dexter Barnes

"Whether she's addressing health care professionals, conference participants, or people one on one, Sue brings a wealth of experience with compassion, directness, and kindness. She helped me understand advocacy, which enabled me to seek better care for my mom."

— Jacquie Bradford, Counselor

"I have the utmost respect and appreciation for the work Sue Stults has done for both me and my family, and for the many other families she has served. Sue came alongside me when my eighty-six-year-old father became ill and was hospitalized more than a dozen times over three years. Her experience and insight in handling the care and challenges of the aging process and decision-making was a tremendous help and blessing."

— Mike Retka, Brier, Washington

"Sue Stults has inspired me in so many ways. She has offered sound advice and information pertinent to grief and loss that I have been able to share with my clients over the death of their beloved pets. Sue is understanding, respectful, and has helped me look at my challenges in a new light. She continues to empower me in dealing with my aging parents. When I think of Sue, I smile, even during difficult times. My day is always better with a hug from her. Thank you, Sue!"

— Tommie Abendroth, Bothell, Washington

"*Reaching Beyond the Rail* has prepared me for the future. After watching the stress my mom experienced in caring for my grandmother for five years, I have dreaded my parents aging and what my role may be in their care. Now that they are beginning to need more assistance, I found this book invaluable for giving me a reality check of what lies ahead, and how I can survive it and provide the best end-of-life experiences possible for my parents."

— Tyler R. Tichelaar, PhD and Award-Winning Author
of *Narrow Lives* and *The Best Place*

"Sue Stults shares the truths about caring for your parents or loved ones as they age. She doesn't hold back from the difficulties, but she also offers guidance for how to do it gracefully so your final experiences with your parents are meaningful and leave you knowing you did the best you could."

— Nicole Gabriel, Author of *Finding Your Inner Truth* and *Stepping Into Your Becoming*

"I wish my family could have had this book during my father's battle with cancer. It would have made all our lives easier. You and your parents deserve the comfort and guidance *Reaching Beyond the Rail* can bring to you."

— Patrick Snow, Publishing Coach and International Best-Selling Author of *Creating Your Own Destiny* and *Boy Entrepreneur*

Reaching Beyond the Rail

THE BLOOD, SWEAT, AND TEARS OF CARING FOR MOM AND DAD

Sue Stults

New York

Reaching Beyond the Rail: The Blood, Sweat, and Tears of Caring for Mom and Dad

Published by:
Aviva Publishing
Lake Placid, NY
518-523-1320
www.avivapubs.com

Address all inquiries to:
Sue Stults
PO Box 82753
Kenmore, WA 98028
425-770-2775
www.ReachingBeyondTheRail.com
www.SueStults.com

ISBN: 978-1-947937-42-0
Library of Congress: 2018906624

Editor: Tyler R. Tichelaar, Superior Book Productions
Cover Designer: Nicole Gabriel, Angel Dog Productions
Interior Book Layout: Nicole Gabriel, Angel Dog Productions
Author Photo: Justin Cutsinger, Motion Film Productions

Every attempt has been made to source properly all quotes.
Printed in the United States of America
First Edition

DEDICATION

To the person who doesn't think he or she can make the journey of walking with mom and dad, the person who doesn't feel he or she has the strength or even the courage, but has a willing heart to try his or her best, the one who is not too proud to ask for help.

"A hero is an ordinary individual who finds the strength to persevere and endure in spite of overwhelming obstacles."

— Christopher Reeve

You're the hero here, so I dedicate this book to you.
I'm praying for you.

ACKNOWLEDGMENTS

I would like to thank the following people for their support, encouragement, and belief in me during the writing of this book and the development of my speaking career.

First and foremost, to my husband Larry, thank you for giving me *wings to fly* and all the time in the world to write. You are the world to me! I love you, honey.

To my children, Jesse, Cameron, Alex, Gloria, Josh, Kylee, Davey, and Ruby. Thank you for your love, support, and encouragement throughout my career change and the writing of this book. All your combined education has made such an impact on my life. Thank you. Love you lots! (And thank you for blessing my life with all those beautiful grandbabies.)

To Kriss, my faithful buddy and friend of thirty-plus years, thank you for all the walks on the Burke Gilman Trail where we continue to try to solve all the world's problems in just about an hour. Thanks for sharing with me, in laughter and tears, throughout life's challenges and victories. We are two peas in a pod.

To Gayle, my dear friend, thank you for working with me so well, for your hard work, and for all the time and energy you give generously! You have encouraged me in so many ways, and I so enjoy your company, both in and out of the office. (We are going to China one day.)

To Pastor Bob and Pastor Steve, thank you for the wisdom and guidance you both have given me and for seeing my potential. What tender-hearted men you are toward those who are hurting.

To Pastor Dwayne, thank you for your excitement about this book! Thank you so much for your help and advice. I appreciate your sincere and genuine compassion for our church, community, and beyond. Love those *hockey tears!*

To the Care Team members at Shoreline Community Church who are so filled with love and compassion for those who are hurting; it has been an honor and a privilege to lead you, and to work shoulder to shoulder together as a team to touch our community with Jesus.

I want to thank my church family at Shoreline Community Church for allowing me to walk alongside many of you through some of the most difficult times of vulnerability and loss in your and your family members' lives. I have learned so much from all of you.

To Lana, the *best* caregiver my mom could have ever had. She loved you as a daughter, you know. Thank you from the bottom of my heart.

To Oma's Mary, thank you, thank you, and thank you, for always being available for Mom. What a wonderful friendship she had with you. I am forever grateful.

To all the great (life) teachers I have had the privilege of meeting, you know who you are. Many of you are in eternity now, but your names and faces will forever remain in my heart. Thank you for teaching me how to love and be loved in return.

To Grandma Jane, my "balcony person," I always wanted to be like you when I grew up. Thank you for believing in me. I sure do miss you.

To Mary Ann, a wonderful and anointed woman of God. Thank you.

To all the strong and beautiful godly women in my life, I say thank you for your wisdom, love, and prayers. Bless you.

To Patrick Snow, thank you for being more than a great publishing coach and speaker. Thank you for being professional and just a regular person with passion to encourage others to find their dreams and dream big, and for allowing Susie Sweet Buns to speak at training seminars. She sends her best.

Thank you, Robin O'Grady, for your graciousness, time, and great work. You stretched me in so many ways I didn't think I could go, but with your gentleness, immense encouragement, and your optimistic attitude, this book was born. I can't thank you enough.

Thank you, Sue Mocker, for your willing heart to allow God to heal your life and use it for his glory. You are an inspiration to all.

To my publishing support team: editor Tyler Tichelaar, book layout and cover designer Nicole Gabriel, Susan Friedmann with Aviva Publishing, and photographer Justin Cutsinger. Thank you for helping me create such an amazing tool for generations to come.

To all my other friends whom I have failed to mention; you know who you are. Please note that I am so thankful for each and every one of you in my life. Your encouragement, big and small, and your prayers and excitement have kept me going. I could not have done this without you.

Above all else, I give God the thanks and the glory for the great things He has done. For *great* is His faithfulness.

Disclaimer

The author, publisher, and vendor of this book make no representations or warranties regarding the outcome or the use to which the information in this book is put. They do not assume any liability for any claims, losses, or damages arising out of the use of this book.

A Note on the Text

Throughout this book I refer to "your parent" because you are likely only caring for one parent at a time. That parent may be male or female, so rather than use the laborious "his or her" and "he and she" for each reference, I have opted to use "their" and "they" to refer to the parent or loved one being cared for and keep the text concise and clear.

Permissions and Citations

Five Wishes information taken from CHOICE Advisory Services, Inc. June 2017–May 2018.

Wong-Baker FACES Foundation (2016). Wong-Baker FACES® Pain Rating Scale. Retrieved October 19, 2016 with permission from http://www.WongBakerFACES.org.

Snyder, Heather. "Love Your Brain." *The Costco Connection Magazine*. June 2017. p. 69.

Warning Signs of Alzheimer's: alz.org/10signs

Preparing for Approaching Death. North Central Florida Hospice, Inc. 1996. Permission Granted.

A NOTE FROM SUE

Many outstanding books are already out there on caring for an aging parent. They are filled with wonderful but copious information. I found as I traveled the path of caregiver that I needed information I could receive in quick increments of time and in smaller doses to make the assimilation easier. As a caregiver, my downtime was limited, and I know yours probably is too, which is why I wrote this book in the fashion I did. I wanted you to reach for this book knowing that anytime of the day you could turn to the Content page to look up a topic to find some helpful tips, encouraging words, and some practical solutions.

Of course, I would encourage you to read my book from cover to cover because there is a lot to learn, and the beginning chapters lay a great foundation to begin with, but I know your time is limited so glean as much as you can. All my stories are true, but names have been changed to protect individuals' privacy. Permission to use their stories has been given to me because they believe I can help many others by sharing them. What bold and courageous people they all are!

CONTENTS

FOREWORD

As young children growing up, we see our parents as vibrant, invincible superheroes able to overcome whatever challenges life sends their way. In my case, I was the fourth of five children and both of my parents were quite active. As I grew up, left home, went off to college, and finally settled as an adult on the other side of the country, I did not see my parents as much as I wanted to. With each visit over the years, I noticed they had more wrinkles, less energy, and were slowing down. This saddened me, but I still felt I would have many more years and visits with them.

Then my life changed forever. Not only was my mother's dementia getting way worse, but my seventy-three-year-old father was diagnosed with pancreatic cancer. Thankfully, through all of this, my eldest sister, Margaret, who is a doctor, spearheaded my parents' care.

I made several trips to Florida to visit Dad in his final months. During these visits, I was the one in charge of taking him to and from his doctors' appointments, setting up new appointments for him, and picking up his medications. When my other siblings were visiting they were also in charge, and we all faced the same overwhelming task of properly caring for Dad. Throughout this time, I was sick to my stomach due to his prognosis, felt overwhelmed, and was experiencing to the full the early stages of grief. As a result, I think the only thing I was able to give to my dad was love and compassion. I was certainly not organized, and I was often unprepared when doctors asked me questions about his care and progress (or lack thereof). Mostly, I was grief-stricken and overwhelmed with the enormous responsibility of keeping his care completely organized.

After a nine-month battle, my father passed and the healing process began for our family. As hard as it was—and continues to be—had we known about *Reaching Beyond the Rail* then, I am 100 percent convinced our family would have accessed its resources, and we would have had a better experience. We could have spent more time being in the present moment with Dad, and less time searching for answers, trying to find doctor information, and being overwhelmed with scheduling all of his appointments. At the end of the day, being more organized would have made it a less stressful experience and allowed all of us siblings who cared for Dad in his last year to have enjoyed more quality time with him.

This book should be required reading for every adult and every household with someone taking medications for any condition. It is a godsend, and it wasn't just put together on short notice; this book has evolved out of Sue's own experience in losing her father.

After experiencing the death of her father, Sue realized what a difficult and tumultuous journey it was to care for a loved one. Lacking skills and an understanding of medical and legal terminology, she felt completely unequipped for the task. Then she began to ask, "Why have people been walking through this alone?"

What she discovered was that there is a lot to learn about care-giving for a parent beyond the physical element. There are legal matters to deal with, the need to create a family support team, and final affairs to be arranged, and that's just the tip of the iceberg. Successful people are resourceful and seek out answers.

In this powerful book by Sue Stults, and her companion book *The Personal Health Care Manual*, you will gain knowledge and insight into how to become better prepared to assist your ill and aging parents with their growing needs and concerns.

In *Reaching Beyond the Rail*, Sue Stults provides you with great tools for a new toolkit, including simple yet timely reminders. Sue's words of *respect, honor, and dignity* fill the pages, and her compassion for humanity is woven throughout this very thought-provoking book.

When you follow this book's formulas, you will discover you are *not* alone. People, tools, tips, and strategies are there to help you along the way. You will learn specific strategies and the skills to achieve caring for your parent with success.

As you read this book, you will learn that you are capable of more than you believe. Let *Reaching Beyond the Rail* be *your* driving force to assist you in becoming a better advocate and support for your loved one.

Sue's compassion and voice is echoed on each page as she guides and educates you and your family through the blood, sweat, and tears of caring for *your* mom and dad. So get ready for an amazing journey because, with this book, you are well on your way to navigating the difficult challenges and roadblocks that are sure to occur as you *reach beyond the rail.*

I challenge you not only to read this book, but to purchase your own personal copy of Sue's *The Personal Health Care Manual* for your family. Your loved ones, doctors, and the other caretakers supporting your family in your time of need will be glad you did.

Patrick Snow

Publishing Coach and Best-Selling Author of *Creating Your Own Destiny*

www.PatrickSnow.com

INTRODUCTION

For many of you, your caregiving journey has already begun. You are already engaged in some form of oversight or care for a parent, or maybe, quite possibly, both parents. Perhaps your parent has been ill for several years or they have just been handed a new diagnosis. The fact of the matter is that you have reached the point of needing some help and advice on what to do next.

I found myself in the same situation when my father announced he had lung cancer in December 1998. The unknown future was very frightening to me, so I decided to educate myself about his disease. I learned about death and dying and what role I needed to play in his care. I also discovered that the information I learned and put into action helped to remove my fears and allowed me to engage more actively in the journey that lay ahead. I believe *you can't fight a battle unless you know who your enemy is.*

This book will answer many of the questions you may be asking and provide you clarity and comfort that will relieve your potential crisis.

Are you sad that your parent is ill and may not get better? Are you overwhelmed with the thought of the challenges ahead? Are you weary in body, mind, and spirit? Are you confused about what you should do or where you should turn for support and answers? Do you know where to go for help to assist you on this journey? Are you running on fumes, and do you feel all alone? Do you have support to help you cope?

I, too, have walked that road with my parents. I understand the stress, frustration, and pain, and I will never forget the journey. I still recall the heavy emotional and physical weight and the fear of the huge responsibility placed on me that I wasn't even sure I wanted or could handle.

I remember all the gains and all the losses my parents experienced, so I want to help *you* recognize them and be able to respond rather than react to them. I want you to know I am here in the trenches with you as you *reach beyond the rail* to care for your mom and dad.

So here *you* are now, searching for answers and support. As you dare to reach beyond your parent's La-Z-Boy recliner or bedrail, I encourage you to use this book for guidance in navigating through new terminology, improving your communication and advocacy skills, and finding support within and outside of your family. This book will teach you all of this and so much more!

You see, your job is not to fix your parent nor cure the illness, but to walk with your parent and help to the end of their days. You will learn what it means to inspire your parent and those around you with the use of *respect, honor, and dignity,* which are critical themes throughout this book.

Also, being willing to educate yourself is vital, and it's a gift to the individual you are caring for. *Keep in mind that you are never too old to learn a new trick or two, and always remain flexible.* Learning new terminology and how to find good support are just a few of the many skill sets you will obtain in the chapters ahead.

There will be times on this journey when you will feel very much alone and overburdened. I am here to encourage you with the hope that you will be able to finish this journey with the sense that you helped your parent to the best of your ability and did all you could.

Consider purchasing the companion manual to this book, *The Personal Health Care Manual.* In it, you will find that I have already done the hard work for you, so all you need to do is fill in the blanks. Having all of your parents' current medical information in one location at your fingertips, including a current list of medications and emergency phone numbers, such as those of physicians, specialists, and family members, is such a relief in the potentially critical situations ahead of you. Having *immediate access* to this information, compiled and in *one location* that any family member can reach for, is what you will need.

Information on how to contact me and how to receive your copy of the manual can be found in the back of this book.

I wish you much strength, courage, and ultimately joy in your journey, with the knowledge that you did the best you could in the end.

Finish well my friend.

Sue Stults

Sue Stults

GROWING OLD

The fairest lilies droop at eventide,
The sweetest roses fall from off the stem;
The rarest things on earth cannot abide,
And we are passing, too, away like them;
We're growing old.

We had our dreams, those rosy dreams of youth;
They faded, and 'twas well. This after prime
Hath brought us fuller hopes; and yet, forsooth,
We drop a tear now in this latter time
To think we're old.

We smile at those poor fancies of the past—
A saddened smile, almost akin to pain;
Those high desires, those purposes so vast,
Ah, our poor hearts! They cannot come again;
We're growing old.
Old? Well, the heavens are old; this earth is too;
Old wine is best, maturest fruit most sweet;
Much have we lost, more gained, although 'tis true
We tread life's way with most uncertain feet.
We're growing old.

We move along, and scatter as we pace,
Soft graces, tender hopes on every hand;

At last, with gray-streaked hair and hollow face,
We step across the boundary of the land
Where none are old.

— April 15, 1893, printed in *The Exchange Newspaper*
(Courtesy of my beloved friend, Helen Markwart)

CHAPTER 1

PREPARING FOR THE JOURNEY

"The journey of a thousand miles begins with one step."

— Lao Tzu

WHERE TO BEGIN

I'm so glad you are here, so let's get started! You have reached for this book in the hope it will give you some sense of what to do now. Maybe someone recommended it to you or you have attended one of my lectures or workshops and purchased it for yourself. It doesn't matter how you got to this point; I'm just glad you did. Welcome!

My hope is you will find wisdom, strength, and many answers to the questions you are seeking as you navigate through the journey of caring for your mom, dad, or a loved one. My ultimate intention is to fill you with strength, knowledge, and hope, and to walk alongside you and your parent until the sun goes down. My hope is you will be left standing upright on your own two feet, knowing you did the very best you could for your parent and that you were able to finish the journey *with peace in your mind, body, and spirit.*

Each journey is different because its travelers and circumstances are different. You will discover many similarities between what I share in this book and your own personal experiences. You will also experience situations unique to you and your family, and that is okay. The journey is different for each.

Keep in mind that a host of different people and relationships will be involved with your parent. Each individual family member, each support team, and each relationship along the way will have its own challenges and strengths. Each person involved has come with their own story, frame of reference, and emotions. An important point to remember, and to remind one another of, is that jealousy, arrogance, control, and manipulation have no place on this path. Learn to observe quietly and be grateful for the good friendships your parent has with others, and don't forget that *your* relationship with your parent is *just* as important.

Recognizing and accepting that a time comes when caring for someone else becomes all about them can be a real reality check. Surprise! It's not about *you* anymore. It is so important that you hear me when I say this so I will repeat it: *It's not about you anymore!* That's right. Let me explain. As your parent's health continues to take a turn for the worse, they may seem less interested in *your* world. Try not to take it personally. It doesn't mean you aren't needed anymore or that you aren't important to your parent. On the contrary, you are now needed more than ever. What you need to be aware of is that the world your parent is currently living in is about to get smaller, and just the habits and rituals of daily life are becoming more challenging for them.

For some elderly people, victory is found in just being able to swing their feet over the side of the bed in the morning, whereas in younger days, they could easily get out of bed each morning. As we age, our bodies begin to show wear, and this wear is exacerbated further by illness. We don't move as fast as we used to, or hear as well as we could in the past, and sometimes, even making simple decisions becomes difficult. Sometimes, the reaction to time itself is not what it used to be, and all of these things can begin to add up. It's hard enough to admit it to yourself, let alone to your children, that you're having increased difficulty with these things. This is where using *respect, honor, and dignity* comes in.

You will read repeatedly in this book about these three monumentally important words: *respect, honor, and dignity.* As you practice using the skill sets attached to the meaning of these words, you will begin to recognize when and how these tools can assist you in making things easier.

PREPARING FOR THE JOURNEY

You will need to be prepared for what lies ahead of you. In some ways, there is really no way to prepare yourself since experience is the great teacher; however, certain events will occur that you will need to be as prepared as possible for; you will also need to recognize that unexpected things will happen as well, so you must remain flexible along the way.

A great story that illustrates this point is about my dear friend Margaret, who was like a second mother to me back in my late teens. I had dated her son for a couple of years, and after my relationship with him ended, I moved on. However, my relationship with his mother Margaret was something that would never disappear as far as she and I were concerned. We became a mother and daughter of the heart. Her complexion was fair, and she was silver-haired, blue-eyed, and from the South. I was brown-haired, brown-eyed, and had just a smidgen of German stubbornness. Often, when we were asked whether we were mother and daughter, we would just shake our heads yes, agree, and then giggle. We shared a very special love between us. We were about forty years apart, but our friendship had no age boundary.

As Margaret got up in years, her life took on some new challenges. Her husband and helpmate passed away within just a few years of buying their new home located in a serene and beautiful senior living community. Shortly after, she was diagnosed with breast cancer, which was followed by a double mastectomy surgery. If that wasn't enough, she had suffered years of intense bone-on-bone pain in both knees. With her family's encouragement, she agreed to have surgery to replace both knees, which was also one of her late husband's wishes for her. The surgery went well, but things quickly changed.

Within a couple of hours of her surgery, both of Margaret's knees dislocated. At that point, the doctors proceeded to wrap both legs from her hips to her ankles with casts to prevent any further movement. Prior to the surgery, Margaret's consultation with the doctor was very promising. The doctor informed her of the surgical procedure and explained the recovery plan, which included rehabilitation. But Margaret and her family were not prepared for this outcome. It changed everything, physically and emotionally.

The original plan after Margaret's surgery was to begin physical therapy within the first couple of hours right there in the hospital room. Her legs were to be placed on a machine that would help her knees to work and bend several times an hour. In the days to come, she would receive more therapy to begin walking so she could return home as soon as possible. It was a great plan.

Everyone was prepared for the original plan, but with the change of circumstance, Margaret and her family were in a tailspin. Why? How many times have you had plans or expectations change their course? Sometimes, a change in circumstance occurs, and then Plan A becomes Plan B, or possibly even Plan F. Sometimes, there is even no plan at all. One recurring theme in this book is *eat, sleep, breathe.* You can use this theme as your prayer and mantra. You will need to remember it when things become difficult.

With Margaret's new situation (both legs in casts), she was forced to forgo returning home that week; instead, she was referred to a rehabilitation center. Under the first plan of recovery, she was told she could return home and, with the help of her family and a walker, manage quite well. Now, having both legs in casts, she was told she would be unable to move, let alone walk for six to eight additional weeks to allow complete healing. Wow! Emotions ran wild that day. Margaret now found her hopes of pain-free knees and a recovery at home to be dashed. Her family was disappointed and charged with the task of finding a place for their mother.

Margaret was transferred to a skilled nursing facility (SNF) located close to her oldest daughter's home. Her daughter had Power of Attorney (POA) for her health care, so the family thought it wise to have her so close. Margaret had a rough time in the nursing facility. The location was great for her family, but it wasn't a place she could call home. It was an old facility, with worn-down furniture and poor lighting. The food was bad, and at times, the daily odors were overwhelming. What made it even worse were the continual residents' cries and the wanderers during the night.

Margaret, unable to move in bed by herself, let alone leave her room, was beside herself. It was like being in prison. She had always been a woman who saw the bright side of things and was the first to engage people in conversation. Now she found herself isolated and alone.

I learned that this particular skilled nursing facility was the only one available to her under her health plan and in that general location at the time of her discharge from the hospital. I remember visiting her later in the evenings when my husband was home to watch our four small children. At her request, I would bring my music and portable tape recorder so I could sing to her while she lay in bed. She would close her eyes as if to disappear into the music and escape this world for just a little while. I was so happy to do it for her and it touched my heart. After two long months, Margaret gratefully returned to the doctor and the casts came off. She was able to return home and resume her life with the aid of in-home care and her family.

As you reach out to offer help to your parent/loved one, remember to be prepared for their response; it may surprise you. Some parents might be grateful for the help you offer because they have been struggling on their own for some time now, so the relief is welcome. Other parents may be angry; they may feel their ability to stay independent is threatened, so they will take it out on everyone else, especially family members who are really trying to help.

And then, there are parents who realize what is soon coming down the pike and desperately want someone to walk alongside them—someone who understands, can help navigate the road ahead, and will love them no matter how rough the road.

Things don't always turn out how we anticipate. Be as prepared as you can, and be aware, too, that you will need to troubleshoot new developments and practice being flexible.

DECISION MAKING

Many important decisions will need to be made on your journey, and sometimes making important decisions takes lengthy discussion. *Take the time* and include your parent in the decision-making process whenever possible. It may be easier to get things accomplished more quickly without them, but it is most important to include them in decisions that directly affect *them* and *their* care!

When a particular issue is too hot of a topic, consider the time of day when your parent is at their best to bring up and discuss the topic. Never leave what needs to be addressed now to another time because a "better time" may never come around. Many times I've heard wives say, "My husband never wanted to talk about it," or "My husband handled all of our affairs," and consequently, the wife had no idea what to do when her husband died.

Spouses are often left behind with no idea where important documents are kept, or how much money is left for current debt and future expenses. Some people have never even written a check before their spouse or parent passed away. Depending on who held the financial role in the home, this situation could be a great burden on the surviving spouse during a very fragile time.

Likewise, it is equally important to inform *your* adult children about family circumstances. Too often, parents wait to inform their grown children of their household affairs, including their financial and final wishes. *Parents tend to wait until some sort of health crisis occurs* before having "the talk" with their children. Once again, as stated previously in this book, I encourage you to consider purchasing the companion manual to this book, *The Personal Health Care Manual*, for your family. The manual can be reviewed by everyone involved in care, and it is a helpful way to stay current on new developments and keep everyone apprised of progress and/or setbacks.

The manual becomes your voice when you don't have one. It is in a notebook format with pages to fill in all of your medical information, doctors' phone numbers, emergency contact numbers, and copies of identification and medical cards. It also contains sections for including copies of important documents such as your Living Will, Powers of Attorney, information on hospice, your final wishes, and much, much more. What took me many years to organize and compile is now completed in an easy-to-follow format for *you* to utilize and refer to when you need it.

Here are a few comments I have received regarding the manual:

"I have been using Sue's book, *The Personal Health Care Manual*, for the past two years for an elderly uncle and it has been of invaluable help to me. Important information is right at my fingertips when I need it. I highly recommend this important tool for everyone." — Kriss Richardson, Chaplain

"Sue has simplified the process of having all pertinent information at your fingertips when you need it most. Her book, *The Personal Health Care Manual*, is such a useful tool that also encourages empathy of the patient's need for dignity through the end of life process. The manual is an indispensable tool to all caretakers." — Nancy Engel, AVP Branch Manager

On a different note, it is important to acknowledge that open and supportive communication by all will be the key to harmonious and best outcomes for your parent because there may possibly be other people involved in making important decisions on your parent's behalf. The more people involved in the decision-making process, the better the communication will need to be. Communication is a skill and an art, and it will be necessary for getting the job done well. Communication can be done one of two ways: "dictatorship," in which one person designates tasks and is at the top of the hierarchal scale, or "dialogue," in which all parties are involved in the process of designating tasks and discussing options. I would suggest using dialogue. I also recommend staying open to learning as you go and listening well to all involved parties before jumping in too fast with your own words or agenda.

THE AWFUL CHRISTMAS STORY

Our home was bustling with busyness one particular morning getting ready for my father and his girlfriend, Bonnie, to arrive for our annual celebration together. It was the one day each year when Christmas and Hanukkah eclipsed at my house. My father, whom our four small children knew as Opa (German for "grandfather"), would drive from Bellingham down to our home in Bothell to spend the day playing games, eating dinner with homemade rolls, and opening wonderful presents with sounds of delight.

My brother, who usually was not in attendance, decided to join us, and we were all excited he had. As I finished the final touches around the house and checked my dinner in the oven, I felt for once I was on top of the holiday. Everything was going just as planned, and the children and dinner would all be ready on time. My father was always early, so this time I was going to be ready. I even thought this time the house and dinner table seemed even better dressed than last year. I was feeling really good about the day and the festivities to come.

My father and Bonnie arrived, and soon after, so did my brother. We all pitched in with unloading the bags and packages from their cars. Soon we were all chatting and hugging our hellos to one another. As I lit the candles on the dinner table and moved to the living room, we all began to gather and settle in. The children were beaming with excitement and anticipation. Dinner still had some time to cook, so we decided to open our gifts, which were overflowing from under the tree. My father, who was always the "King of the Jungle" no matter where he was, took the lead. As he stood by the hearth of the fireplace, he began.

One by one, he handed each one of us a sealed white envelope with our names neatly printed on the front. We were then instructed to open them one at a time and read them out loud so all could hear, beginning with our youngest child, who was nine at the time.

As my youngest son and I sat together on the floor at the foot of my husband's chair, he began to open his envelope and I leaned in close. We were all filled with curiosity and wonder.

The words slowly began to emerge out of my young and innocent son's mouth. I leaned in closer because I thought he was having trouble reading the handwriting. So I began to read it out loud… "Dear David" it said, "You have been a bad little boy…"! I froze in horror! What kind of letter was this? Definitely not one from the Santa Claus I know! Realizing this was not a joke and Santa (aka my father) was serious, I thought to myself, *Could it be we are all being punished and shamed in front of one another* (one of my father's favorite discipline techniques) *just because we didn't send our "Dear Santa" letters to my father on time.*

My father wanted us all to open our letters, but we were paralyzed with disbelief by such a horrific and hurtful act. Not knowing what else these letters might say and to protect David and the rest of us from any more hurt, my husband stood to his feet in anger, glared at my father, and ordered this activity to stop. As my husband finished his words, he then tore the unopened white envelope (still in his hand) in half, as if to say, "Enough is enough!" At that very moment, my father rose again to his feet and loudly blurted out, "I have cancer and it's inoperable!" I felt like I was in a dream. Did I just hear what I thought I had heard? He then ordered the children out of the room and *demanded* to speak with his family.

Still stunned and stinging from my father's words and his rude demeanor, my brother, husband, Bonnie, and I remained seated, waiting for who knows what would come next—perhaps another below-the-belt blow. My father went on to state that he only wanted my brother and me in the room, and no other intruders were allowed.

I felt pulled in half by that command as my husband was ordered to leave the room. My husband, however, knew by then that it was no use even to try to communicate with my father. As my father, a retired military man, barked out the orders, I silently saluted, numb from my brain to my fingertips and toes. My demanding father then reported that my brother and I were required to be in the city of Bellingham, which was north from our home, in two days. We were informed that there were papers to be signed and documents to discuss. We were to spend the entire day reviewing these matters, and with that, he stated he was leaving to head back to his home in Bellingham.

I was still feeling caught in a bad dream, and now it just kept getting worse. I stared out into nowhere as I watched him gather his things. I felt numb all over. There was no discussion about the cancer. No discussion of what kind, or where it was located, of how big it was, or how much time *we* had, whether he was in pain, or whether he was feeling scared or sad. Nothing.

I wanted to cry out loud. *I am scared and sad. I am! I am...!*

Outside we stood, my brother and I, frozen in time as we watched my father and Bonnie as they climbed into their car. As I glanced one last time at Bonnie, I noticed her large, pain-filled eyes. Her body was silent, but her eyes spoke volumes, as if to say, "I am *so* sorry. I didn't know he was going to tell you like this, *especially* today, of all days. Really, *I am so very sorry.*"

With the red glow of the taillights fading away up the driveway, my brother finally found his voice and managed to say these sad and lonely words, "We're going to be orphans." We hugged, but no more words were exchanged and he headed for his car. Then, as his car disappeared up the driveway, *that's* when it happened.

Out of my innermost being came this violent, painful, and uncontrollable sobbing that rose up from my gut and out through my mouth, nose, and eyes. It was an unknown experience for me. It was so powerful that it doubled me over, and I needed to support myself by leaning against a wooden post, which supported the porch above me. I stood there wailing in emotional pain for several minutes, which felt like hours suspended in time. I sobbed and moaned from a place I had never known before. I stood there in the drizzling rain for perhaps ten minutes, lost in deep sorrow. The tears just poured out and the pain in my gut just yelled!

When my body finally stopped reeling from tears and emotion, I realized I had no idea where my husband and four children were. I had been so caught up with everything that I had no idea what was happening to *my* family and what they might be going through.

I found my husband in his office downstairs and the three boys playing in the family room together. I found no signs of the oldest, my daughter. Checking the house, room by room, in a bit of a panic, I discovered her bedroom window open a bit with the screen removed. Fear filled my mind. Did she run after my father's car? Did she really understand what had just happened in our living room? I was now in full panic mode.

What do we do now? I phoned a neighbor up the street to see whether she had gone there, but she hadn't. I wanted to get in the car to go looking for her because I was afraid for her. I was just a mess with all that was happening. Thankfully, my dear husband helped settle me down. He assured me that our daughter would be okay, and she had probably just needed to walk or run it all off. He reminded me that she was fifteen and very responsible.

As I began to shut off the oven and turn off the stove for the dinner we never had, I tried to think of a way to salvage the day. The gifts under the tree would have to wait for another day because nobody felt like celebrating. Soon after, I heard the front door open and there, in dripping wet clothes, stood my daughter with tears streaming down her rosy pink cheeks.

You see, she was the oldest, so she and my father went way back; they had history together. She was the very first grandchild, and he was so thrilled to be her opa (grandfather).

I was thirty-nine when my father made his cancer announcement; I wasn't too sure I was going to make it through, especially with all the unknowns ahead. However, sometimes it's the things you think will destroy you that end up making you even stronger.

HELPFUL TIP 1

With multiple doctors, specialists, and care providers involved in the health care of your parent, you will need to organize and consolidate contact information and health care details in one place for sake of ease. *The Personal Health Care Manual* is that tool. Go to SueStults.com for more information or to contact me.

CHAPTER 2

SUPPORTING MOM AND DAD

"When we are no longer able to change a situation,
we are challenged to change ourselves."

— Viktor E. Frankl

How well do you know how to be supportive of your mom or dad? This may not be a question you have thought about until now. Have you laid the foundation over the years of good communication with your folks? The communication skills you have used with your parents in the past may not necessarily apply now, and communication may become more difficult if they are struggling with illnesses or have become more resistant to change. Let me give you a word of wisdom here: *Your parent never deserves shaming, scolding, or harsh discipline.* If your parents have become unsuccessful at a task, big or small, regardless, give them gentle guidance.

Don't humiliate them by treating them like children; they are merely aging adults. What they really need now more than ever is your love and support and your willingness to give them some of your time to help them. Your parents may be starting to realize or possibly already know that the sun is beginning to set in their lives and that the only thing they really have left is time. *Learn to give your parents the time they need.*

Your parents' world is slowing way down and possibly all that is left in their day is shuffling from the recliner to the bathroom and the bed. Your parents may need to nap more or may begin sleeping in longer in the morning. Their appetite may begin to change and you may notice them eating less. These are all natural signs that the body begins to experience and are indicators that *change* is indeed on the horizon. It is important that you pay attention to these signs and make note of them. Later, in Chapter 4: Navigating the Road Signs, we will talk more clearly about recognizing and learning to cope with changes and other accompanying issues that may surface during the process.

As you begin practicing new skills or honing the skills you already have, remember to be patient and compassionate. *Respect, honor, and dignity will be your goal.* Your parent may have a whole host of personal thoughts and feelings about what is happening to them. They may feel prideful, powerless, and frightened, and they may resist your help even though they desperately need it.

The more patience and compassion you can model for your parent, the more likely they are to share their feelings and experiences with you so you can be of maximum help. This can be increasingly difficult as the stress from the responsibility of caregiving mounts heavily on your shoulders. Sometimes the stress becomes so intense and frustrating that it could potentially lead to inappropriate and aggressive behavior on the part of the caregiver. Which brings me to the next topic of discussion: elder abuse.

ELDER ABUSE

There is never a good time to talk about elder abuse. Unfortunately, it happens, so I want you to understand and be aware of what behaviors constitute elder abuse. Please remember, there is *never* a time or place to *discipline* your parent! Disciplining, scolding, shaming, or demeaning your parent for not being able to do better, do more, or do things differently can be considered *abusive* and cause permanent damage to your relationship and your parent's wellbeing.

While correcting or redirecting your parent's behavior, never act like you are *disciplining* them. Please note the distinction I made between the words correction and discipline. Your parents are not your children even if they seem to be acting childlike.

Everyone knows what childish behavior looks and feels like. We have witnessed it in others and maybe even ourselves. I know I have behaved childishly at times, and I'm not proud of it, but it has happened. Here again is another opportunity for me to remind you of the three very important words: *respect, honor, and dignity.*

You will see these words several times throughout this book. My intention is to brand them into your mind. As you walk the road home with your parent, difficult situations will certainly arise in which you will either choose to react or respond. Our minds often take charge in difficult circumstances, so if you prepare ahead of time, you will have the ability to respond *mindfully* rather than react to the stress you are sure to experience.

Some examples of elder abuse include yelling, shouting, scolding, or shaming. These reactions are never the answer. Also, withholding food, slapping, hitting, shaking, and pulling hair are all wrong. Locking someone in a bedroom or a house all alone with no telephone is also wrong. You may be wondering whether these things actually happen or whether I am exaggerating. I wish I was, but I am not. As I learned of these horrific travesties committed against our elders and even witnessed some of them myself, I was forced to open my eyes. I feel compelled to share this information with you so you can see it, respond to it, and potentially pass on your knowledge to others. William's story is an example of one such situation that I experienced in my work.

WILLIAM'S STORY

William was a kind and gentle old man whom I had met a few years back. He owned his own home in a quaint, little tourist town up north. William was a widower for many years and got along just fine on his own. The grocery store was within walking distance and a handful of small town restaurants lined the sidewalks along the way. This little town was perfect for all his needs.

William had two grown children, a daughter and a son. The daughter and he were estranged for many years, but the son was still very much in contact. William and his son's relationship grew closer in his later years. One spring, his son was diagnosed with cancer. The disease had advanced to the point where the son asked his father whether he could come home and live his last months with him in the family home. William said yes.

For a few weeks, William cared for his son's needs, but the task got harder. He too, was aging, and his abilities were becoming limited. William needed some help, so he asked one of his nephews for help. They, too, were close, so it was something the nephew felt he could do for his favorite uncle. Within a week, the nephew had moved in and was eager to help. It was a sacrifice for his nephew and William knew it.

I began visiting them and soon was helping out where I could. Most of my time was spent just listening. Hugs and kisses were always welcomed, and many cups of coffee were shared. William's son was assigned to hospice and the team rotated in and out as the days passed by—what a wonderful addition to the family the hospice workers were.

One evening, William's son took a turn for the worse, and by late morning the following day, he passed away. It was a tough day. In the ensuing days and weeks, William's nephew began to see how fragile his uncle had become. The fun uncle he remembered was now showing signs of forgetfulness, incontinence, and financial problems. The nephew also realized his uncle was no longer capable of living on his own. William had done such a great job hiding his many troubles during his son's illness, but now with his nephew being there around the clock, day in and day out, the evidence was apparent.

I, too, noted William's decline and gave advice on elder care. However, much of the advice I gave was ignored because William's nephew was unable or *unwilling* to take proper action.

Time went on and William's house was sold. He and his nephew moved into a small rental about five miles up the road. I was never notified of the new location until I ran into a mutual friend who informed me of the new address. Soon after, I made a visit. When William's nephew opened the door, he was very surprised to see me standing there. I heard William in the background, and he waved me in. I was a bit shocked when I saw him; he looked unkempt and a bit disheveled. This really concerned me.

I began to visit more frequently, and soon I found William locked in the house and all alone. As time marched on, things went from bad to worse rather quickly. Red flags of concern were everywhere in my mind. My concern for my friend was great! What I began to realize was that William was experiencing elder abuse.

What happened from there is so lengthy and painful that I have chosen not to continue with the story. I learned a lot through this experience, and I lost a dear friend in the process. If you see or even suspect elder abuse happening, call the Elder Abuse Hotline. If you don't call, who will? Dial 911 or the emergency department in your area. Call the police department. Be brave and tell them what you know. It may be a matter of life or death.

LEARNING TO PRACTICE BEING PRESENT

As you give your time to your parent, you will also want to practice being present, truly present, in an effort to be more aware of what the needs and challenges are in caring for them. In a world where everything seems to be moving so fast and distractions like technology keep us so busy, being present and being an intentional listener can be difficult.

One way to be an intentional and active listener is to watch your parent's facial expressions as they talk about their day. As you listen with *both* ears, you will hear about and learn of their victories and disappointments. You may even discover more about what really makes them who they are. As I became more involved with my mom's health issues and care, I learned a lot more about her.

When my mother willingly hung up her car keys and stopped driving (more about when it is time to take the keys in Chapter 5), I became her transportation. As we drove together to the doctor's office, grocery store, and drugstore, it became an adventure. Sometimes, our time together running errands was the only time she ever got out of the house. What a gift to have those adventures together! There were also times when I would take her for rides just to get her out of the house and give her a change of scenery, and she just loved it.

When my mother's neighbors would ask where she was off to, she would reply with a little snicker and a smile, saying, "Oh, Sue's taking me for a *ride* again." We started out by driving a couple of hours away, or sometimes we would take a fifteen-minute ride, depending on her energy level that particular day. I began to talk less and listen more. Somehow, the car transformed into the "Cone of Silence," where anything could be talked about in the safety of the front seat of my Subaru. We both learned to enjoy this time together so much.

On occasion, the drive would take us to the drive-thru at Starbucks, to Mickey D's for a strawberry ice cream sundae, or down Locust Way to gaze upon the bright red, orange, and yellow autumn leaves.

I learned quickly to keep the radio off, let the conversation meander where it would, and let Mom lead the conversations when she wanted. Many times, I heard her soft voice reciting the Latin names of the trees and bushes we drove past. I thought at first she did this for me so I could learn and identify these trees and bushes, but I later realized it was for her; she was just processing and thinking out loud. Now, looking back, I really don't think she even realized she was doing it.

For over two decades, mom was a plant propagator, working in wholesale plant nurseries in Western Washington. She was in her late thirties when she learned the trade. Her boss, a notable Dutchman named Arie Oosterwick, had long been in the nursery industry. She learned the secrets of the trade and was a hard-working employee who gave her all to her work. She was one of the few in her industry who truly loved her work. This reciting of the Latin names of trees was a normal behavior for her after many years of studying and developing expertise in her field.

Looking back, sitting behind the warm windshield of the car when the weather was good and not too hot was one of the best outings we would enjoy together. We had no appointments to hurry off to, no agenda, and no particular time to return home. It seemed then that we had all the time in the world together (or so I led her to believe).

As my mom's health declined, I knew our rides together were getting shorter and shorter and would eventually come to an end. It became more difficult to get her ready and into the car, and being too far from her private bathroom became a major concern for her, so we began exploring new ways to enjoy each other's company.

Sometimes, just sitting together in silence was all she needed, and we learned together to be at peace and rest with that. Words don't always need to be spoken, and the TV doesn't always have to be on to feel like you're connecting with someone. The most important thing is just to be present. Take the time to slow down and spend time with your parent. Give your parent your undivided attention and practice being present. It is something you will never regret.

INTENTIONAL/ACTIVE LISTENING

It is so important to listen with intent to your parent, and you will also need to learn how to solicit information. Also, as stated before, be aware of your parents' expressions. One of the best ways to get information is to ask questions and then listen and watch closely. Your conversation could go something like this:

"Dad, I've noticed that you are grimacing this morning; are you in any pain?" Now listen for his response.

Another great way to get information about someone's pain level is to use the same method used by health care professionals, i.e., the pain scale.

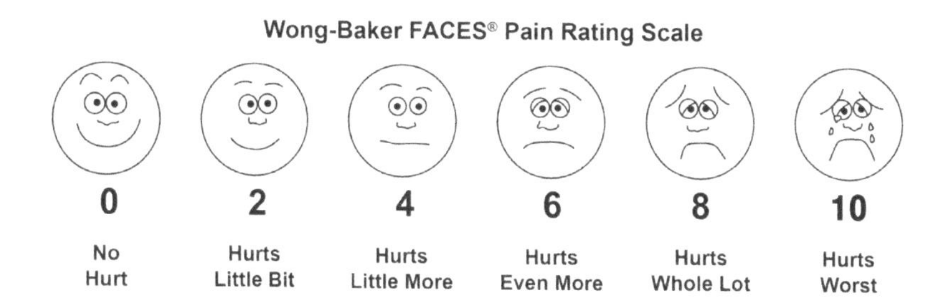

Try asking your parent, "On a scale of 1-10, Dad, 1 being no pain and 10 being the worst pain ever, what number would you give your pain right now?" Let him respond. Then validate the pain by saying something like: "I'm sorry you're in pain. Can I get you something for it, or call your doctor for you?" Another useful statement might be: "Is there something I can do for you?"

As your parent's health changes, their level of pain may also increase. With the increase of pain usually comes more medication and potentially more powerful drugs to control the pain or illness. This means you must keep a watchful eye on your parents' prescribed medication to be sure it is being taken correctly. I have found that many people hold off on taking their pain medication until the pain worsens because they fear becoming addicted, rather than taking the medication to stay ahead of the pain. Unmanaged pain is like an out-of-control freight train speeding down the tracks. The longer and faster the train is allowed to run, the more strength, time, and endurance it will take to stop it. Likewise, it takes an enormous effort to try to control pain that has gotten out of control.

You may also find yourself in the position of being an advocate for your parent when it comes to pain control and medication since your parent may no longer have a voice of their own. When your parent no longer has a voice, you must become their voice. Let me say that again: *When your parent no longer has a voice, you must become their voice.* They are counting on you to be heard! When I wrote my first manual, *My Personal Health Care Notebook* (later revised and renamed *The Personal Health Care Manual*), back in 2010, I stated, "*This book is Your Voice when you have none.*"

As illness and aging encroach, we can grow weary and may not have the strength or stamina to fend for ourselves. Can *you* be *that* voice? Having the proper documents in order and ahead of time for your parent can ensure that *their* voice is heard when they have none. While there is time, help your parent get these important things in place so you will be ready and can understand your parent's directives and desires ahead of time if at all possible. You will be glad you did.

Intentional listening means you have your ears and eyes open, you are asking important questions, and you are learning as much as you can about your parent now, as opposed to later. Intentional listening means you are taking responsibility to get important things in place while your parent can still help you if possible, and that you are advocating when necessary for your parent because you are aware of their responses and needs.

It doesn't take much to listen, but it does mean putting your ears on and at times learning to hold your tongue. Listening is one of the greatest tools we have to understanding why people do what they do. It is something we all need a lesson in at times.

Take a moment and jot down three areas in which you need to learn to listen better:

1. ______________________________

2. ______________________________

3. ______________________________

As you improve your listening skills, you will become all the richer, and you will even relearn things you may have forgotten! Intentional and active listening may be difficult, but it will be well worth it in the end.

BITTERNESS

Bitterness is like a weed that can take root in your heart and eat you alive. My father was the first of my parents to have his health decline. His whole life he had struggled with lung issues, and being a smoker for more than thirty years didn't help. At age fifty-five, his lungs collapsed while he was home alone, and after eight hours of struggling on the floor of his apartment, help finally arrived. He managed to survive this horrific ordeal and was given sixteen additional years of life. I call that a miracle! These extra years were our time of reconciliation. My father was a military man and very controlling. Either you liked him or you didn't, and I was acutely aware that I wasn't the only one who knew that about him. After his retirement from the military, he took a job as a border inspector on the US-Canadian border. Soon after, my parents' marriage failed and they went their separate ways, as did my brother and I. We all had separate lives and careers, and we pressed forward, trying not to look back at the scars we all carried. When my father received his cancer diagnosis and it came time to speak with my brother about his care, with pointed finger, my brother informed me *he* was to be the financial decision maker and *I* would be the caregiver.

My best advice to you after experiencing the feeling of bitterness myself is to recognize when you are experiencing bitterness in your conversations with others. Take notice of your body language and be aware of your facial expressions. What are your expressions and body language really saying? Your bitterness could easily take root and spread to others, so make a conscious effort to change your attitude right then and there. Stop your negativity and redirect your thoughts so that the bitterness will not take root and strangle your heart or anyone else's.

Trust that though you may not be aware, others might see and feel the bitterness in you. This situation could breed further friction during an already difficult time. Bitterness and negativity are like poison and can make you toxic to others. *Don't* let it take root. Instead, let love and forgiveness have their way. Take a minute to be more aware of your feelings around bitterness. Has it crept into:

- Your conversations with others?
- Your facial expressions?
- Your body language?
- Your tone of voice?
- The volume of your voice?

Many times while I cared for my parents, I had to walk alone because my sibling insisted he was "not available." This began the seed of bitterness in my own heart. *Bitterness is a poison*, and though it may be hard, you must let it go. Don't allow it to fester, and do your best to practice love and forgiveness instead. This may seem hard, but it can be done. I know this because I had to do it myself.

Letting go of bitterness does not negate the importance of addressing inappropriate behavior when it is called for. If your parent or a member of your support team is behaving poorly, tough love may be needed, but be sure to speak the truth in the spirit of love. If correction is necessary, people are much more likely to hear you if you are coming from a place of helpfulness.

When caregiving, remember that your attitude should be focused on *respect, honor, and dignity*. They are the cornerstones everyone involved needs to operate from. There is no sense in trying to change anyone else because you can't. People are who they are, and really, it's not your responsibility to change them. Once you grasp that you can't change anyone else and you will need to accept them as they are, you are on your way to being able to forgive them for their shortcomings and to begin letting go of bitterness.

FORGIVENESS

When my husband and I decided to have a family, our hearts' desire was to raise children who would play well together and respect each other. We wanted to teach our children to become productive, responsible contributors to society. It was important to us that our children would grow up to be givers, not takers. Those were the goals my husband and I had for our little family. Deep in *my* heart was the desire to have a family that was so close that we would learn to laugh and cry together, and to forgive each other as well.

When our children were growing up, we taught them the simple words "I'm sorry" and "I forgive you." These principles were not always easy for my children to practice, but when they did practice them, they experienced joy firsthand when receiving forgiveness from a sibling. Repentance and forgiveness are tools that go a long way in keeping relationships whole and healthy.

Has there ever been a non-repentant heart or a cold attitude in our family? Of course there has, but repentance and a clean heart can melt a frozen heart. It is amazing what forgiveness can do. My prayer is that my children will always be close to each other in heart and that pride will never stand in the way of their love and friendship. Through good and bad times, they can call on each other for support.

Learning to practice forgiveness and to let go of bitterness toward those who aren't available to help can also go a long way in helping you not become toxic and resentful in your heart.

STRESS AND THE BODY

Did you know that when you are experiencing stress, your body goes into the "fight or flight" mode? This means that your large muscle groups take charge, but your brain function goes out the window. It's sort of like when my husband had his first seizure and I called 411, not 911, for emergency assistance. I thought I was in control of the situation until the voice on the other end of the phone asked, "What city and state please?"

Because emergency and stressful situations may cause confusion, it makes sense to have all your medical information in one location in advance. Your medical information should include a current list of medications and emergency phone numbers such as physicians, specialists, and family members. Having this information available decreases stress during critical situations because you have information you need right in front of you.

Stress also takes a huge toll on your body. My mantra here is *eat, sleep, and breathe.* Following these three simple steps may sound simple, but it's not as simple as it sounds when you are trying to focus on caring for your parent. It's important that you make the time to eat each day, that you do your best to get enough sleep, and that you remember to breathe deeply during the course of your day. If your cup isn't full, you will have less energy and will be less able to take care of someone else.

Here is a great experiment to try next time you are with your parent: Pay close attention to your own breathing. You might notice you have the same breathing pattern they do. Stress can cause a shallower breathing pattern, and by not breathing deeply, you can feel more fatigued, sluggish, and foggy-headed. Take some time to practice breathing deeply throughout the day, and be thankful for the new day—it's a gift; that's why it's called the present. God's mercies are new every morning.

When caring for an ill parent, there are many turns and twists in the road. What you learned last month or even yesterday may not work or be good enough for today. There is a constant learning curve when it comes to caregiving because you are dealing with a human being with a potentially progressively debilitating illness. You are also dealing with a human life, which is very precious cargo. Remember the three important words I mentioned in this book's introduction: *respect, honor, and dignity*. I will continue to prompt you with these three words until they permeate your being and your brain remembers them. After repeated exposure to these three words, your body will automatically follow in action.

When new situations arise, you will naturally respond in your usual behavior. If you are having difficulty coping with these new situations and are reacting rather than responding to your parent, remembering *respect, honor, and dignity* is a more healthy and positive response. It will change your heart and attitude and make you happier and healthier in your own mind and body in the long run. (Trust me here.) It can be very easy to get frustrated or even angry with your parent, but keep the three words *respect, honor, and dignity* in the forefront of your mind and they will help melt away your old behaviors and responses so you can be of better and more compassionate service to your parent.

Sometimes, you may find that it can be a real challenge to keep a positive and compassionate attitude, especially when you are not taking care of yourself properly. There are some things you can control, and others you cannot. The goal is just to do the very best you can. I know it can be so hard. I've been there with lack of sleep, no time for a shower or even a meal, or even time enough to take my own medication. At one point, I found myself so exhausted that I just knew I was going to collapse. I could hear the warning bells going off in my head: WARNING! WARNING!

When you get to the end of *your* rope, recognize it so you don't continue decompensating. This point leads to burnout, which we will discuss in detail in the next section. No one purposely sets out to experience burnout, but if you do become burned out (which many of us do), learn to step back and really be honest with yourself and those around you about where you are. You *will* need to allow some help to come in. Believe me when I say *nobody* can care for your mom, spouse, or child as well as you can, but you can't let your pride get in the way once you find yourself standing in the shoes of burnout.

HELPFUL TIP 2

As you add to the new toolkit of skills you are learning so you can help care for your parent, remember to be patient with your parent *and* yourself on the journey. Patience includes putting bitterness on the back burner, practicing forgiveness, and being aware of the signs of stress on your body. Let *respect, honor, and dignity* be your guide.

CHAPTER 3

PROTECTING YOURSELF

"This is a marathon in life. You can't be sprinting all the time or else you wear yourself out. You have to make sure you're taking care of yourself, keeping yourself grounded and not letting every little thing get you worked up."

— Brian Moynihan

By this point in this book, hopefully you have begun to understand many new things. You have learned how to be prepared for the journey of being a caretaker for your parent and that you will be making important and sometimes difficult decisions on their behalf. You have also experienced an awareness of new skills and begun to practice them in order to be of maximum service to support your parent during *their* journey.

So now, the question becomes: What about *you*? How will you protect yourself from common potential challenges that come naturally as a result of taking care of someone else? Challenges like having to put yourself last, getting burned out and exhausted, and balancing your own daily structure and needs with those of your parents?

SELF-CARE

What is self-care and why is it so important and necessary? Don't get self-care mixed up with the care your parents need. This section is for *you*, the caregiver. Even if you might not be the one who feeds and bathes your parent, you are still considered a caregiver if you are helping them out even in the smallest sense. Never underestimate your role, but remember not to inflate it either. Credit belongs where credit is due. Be sure to give credit and thanks to others who are assisting your parent whenever possible. *Self-care is taking a little time for oneself.*

Now, let's talk about *what self-care isn't.* It isn't selfish, and it's not something to feel guilty about, so please read on. Caring for an aging or an ill parent can be tedious, and exhausting. Caregiving for your parent may go on for many years. You will need to pace yourself in order to have energy for the long haul, so if you neglect to give yourself some periodic self-care, you will become ill, worn-out, and of no use to anyone. Trust me on this!

The importance of self-care was made apparent to me when my mom was admitted to the Hospice Unit at Evergreen Hospital. My family was quite sure she was in her last days when she suddenly made a turn around and slowly began to recover. One afternoon while visiting my mom at the hospice unit, I found myself seated at a small round table in the communal kitchen when one of the nurses took a seat across the table from me. We spoke for a bit, and then she expressed her concern. She looked me square in the eye, and with gentle words, she spoke to my heart. She saw my exhaustion—my physical and emotional fatigue. She had seen this before, probably many times over, from the people who flowed through the unit each day. She knew through her own experience that the road and journey ahead for my mom and me had only just begun, especially for me because I would be the caregiver. Her words were sweet but direct, and they cut to my soul and my stubborn mind.

"Sue," she said, "this is not a sprint; it's a marathon. If you continue on the same path you are on now, you *will* get ill and you will not make it."

I had given my all to my mom for the prior year and a half, and I was just plumb exhausted. I had originally thought mom's health was so bad that she wouldn't last as long as she had. Many a day I thought for sure would be her last, but she kept going. Her body was so tired and she labored so hard at times to breathe that I was positive her body, at any minute, would stop the fight, but she just kept going.

Stress and worry can wear you out, and often, you may not realize just how much until you look back in hindsight. Stress and worry will rob you of your own good health, but you can compromise and begin striving for a healthier balance at any point you choose. During the first and second days of my mother's hospice stay, I knew it could very well be her last, but once again, she proved everyone wrong, including the hospice staff. While most people who enter the physical doors of a hospice unit never return home, a few do, and my mom was one of them.

Such a difficult time is a good example of when you need to take better care of yourself. Caring for others can deplete you in many ways, and during especially hard times, you may experience a strong desire to put your personal needs on the back burner. You may forget to take your *own* medications, or drink enough water; you may postpone your dentist appointment, or skip a shower, a meal, or even an oil change in your car. At this point, you need to be healthier than ever.

Everyone's self-care tools are different. Here I have included some additional tools I recommend you use: take a nap, get some exercise, change your routine, and remember to keep a sense of humor. You will learn more about these tools in just a bit, but first let's take a look at the symptoms of burnout.

BURNOUT

It is important to recognize the signs of burnout. In order to do so, you must be honest with yourself about it. You must allow others to step in and help. Burnout isn't like the common cold or flu, so beware. You don't always notice it when you are standing in the middle of it. Here are some symptoms to help you identify whether you are experiencing burnout:

- Feelings of depression
- A sense of ongoing and constant fatigue
- Decreasing interest in work
- Decrease in work production

- Withdrawal from social contacts
- Increase in use of stimulants, drugs, and alcohol
- Increasing fear of death
- A change in eating patterns
- Feelings of helplessness
- Not wanting to get out of bed

The next few sections in this chapter give you some great ideas for how to alleviate some of the stress that comes with the territory of being the caretaker for your parent, especially when you are experiencing some (or all) of these burnout symptoms.

THE ART OF NAPPING

Take a nap daily if possible. Napping is an art form I learned from my husband. Early in our marriage, I became frustrated with my husband and his frequent napping while raising our four children. He was self-employed and his work was seasonal, so during the slow times when the telephone seldom rang, he would take a siesta about mid-day. While I was busy slaving away with children, housework, PTA, Bible study, Tupperware parties, cutting hair, and on and on *and* on, he would nap.

"Nappy time is a happy time" was the cute little saying I would tell our children as I was preparing them for their afternoon naps, *but* it was never intended for my husband, so I resented how he just ignored everything and shut down to take a nap in the middle of our busy day! I thought, *How can he do this?* It drove me crazy, and some days it made me so angry I would steam inside. Well, over the years as I got to know my husband better and tried to understand why he does the things he does, I came to realize that napping was just a part of who he was and perhaps even one of his coping methods.

I thought it was an escape on his part, and in actuality, it *is* a way of escape, but it is more a way of coping with the stress of daily life, a coping mechanism. In a general sense, it is said that napping can actually add years to your life. In the United States, we race the clock every day and become so stressed out because there aren't enough hours in a day to get everything done we think we need to do (or so we think). Even though we have so many appliances to ease our workload, in my opinion, we continue to stuff so much more into our day that we actually make our lives more stressful than we need to.

When our children flew the nest, I began to practice the art of napping and came up with new and improved terms for the types of napping I did. Let me give you some examples: There's the Sunday afternoon nap, the after church and a bite of lunch-out nap, the mid-day nap, the sleepy-time nap, the any day of the week nap, the five-minute catnap (otherwise known as the shuttin' down nap), and the wee little nappy-pooh. And I've saved the best nap of all for last, the big one: the nap when you have too much on your plate so you need to reset and clear your thoughts and give your body time to process it all. I have been known to take a nap alone, but having my husband right next to me is the best kind of nap in the world. (Honey, thanks for teaching me the Art of Napping!)

SWITCHING YOUR ROUTINES

Begin by eating at least two good meals a day. If you can manage three, that's even better. Make a smoothie or a healthy shake and incorporate fruit and vegetables into your day. Make healthy snacks ahead of time and take them with you on the run. Stay away from too much caffeine and sugar because it will drag you down and deplete your energy over the day. Avoid empty calorie foods that will leave you hungry and craving salts and sweets. Also, avoid fast food as your daily staple because it, too, can give you a shorter feeling of satisfaction and can become an unhealthy choice over the long run. I understand there are times for something quick and easy, and that's okay, but be wise when making decisions about the food you eat to fuel your body and brain.

Exercise is a great way to let go and reduce stress. If you have a gym membership, go to the gym. If you don't have one, get one. Any type of physical activity will do you some good. Don't forget to *eat, sleep, and breathe.*

I encourage you to keep your doctor and dentist appointments. You need the follow-up to stay healthy. Don't let your medications run out. Refill them and stay on track. Take care of your own hygiene so you are on your best game and you don't smell.

Remember to keep gas in the car at all times, and get maintenance and oil changes done in a timely manner so your vehicle is always available to you and your parent.

Yes, your parent may need you, but you need to take some healthy steps for yourself.

More difficult times call for increased self-care measures. Like we discussed in Chapter 1, your parents' world is closing in on them and they are going to need you more and more.

LAUGHTER

One day while my mom was still able to be silly and enjoy some good humor, I announced plans for a last-minute evening "hat party."

My sister Monika and her daughter Claudia had come from Germany for a two-week visit, knowing it could quite possibly be their last visit with mom. While they kept Mom occupied at her apartment, I dashed home to gather some supplies. Searching through the old Halloween costume boxes I had stashed away in the basement, I came across numerous silly hats. Grabbing several, I charged back up the stairs. I gathered some yummy treats from my kitchen, watered the plants, loved on my two sweet little dogs, chatted with my husband just a bit, and then kissed him goodbye.

As I left the house, I was grinning from ear to ear in anticipation of the fun evening ahead, and I could almost guarantee my husband was chuckling to himself while shaking his head from side to side as if to say, "Here she goes again."

That evening at Mom's apartment, we had our hat party, and what fun it was. It was a modest gathering of six. The guest list consisted of my sister, my niece, Mom's caregiver Della, a good friend and neighbor from upstairs Martha, and, of course, Mom and me. We all selected our hats from the colorful pile I had brought from home and from random pieces my mom had lying around the apartment. Oh, what a fun time we had together! Silliness was written all over the evening. The laughter we shared that evening was so important. Don't forget to laugh!

We ate small treats, played some of Mom's favorite music, and took several pictures together. What a joy it was for all of us to watch my mom giggle and laugh. I even reached across her walker while she was seated in her "chair of grandeur," wearing her felt hat with the red rose in the center brim, and held her hand while boogieing. Each of us adorned our heads with a hat or crown of choice while casting all cares aside, as if to step out of the reality lurking just around the corner. The escape was good for all of us, including the nice neighbor down the hall, who stopped by just to take our pictures. That day we celebrated life! Soon after, Mom began to spend more time in bed. Laughter is good medicine!

I have a really goofy side that likes to laugh and have fun, and sometimes, that includes telling silly jokes. My father called them "Susie jokes" because, when I was young, I would make them up as I went along. Somehow, I was always the only one laughing because to me they were terribly funny. I've come to realize that as a visual learner, when someone tells me something, I follow along in my head and create pictures. That is exactly what I do when I create my crazy jokes. They come to me in pictures.

The process goes something like this: The giggles begin internally, and sooner or later, usually sooner, they have to come up to the surface. Sometimes, even before I can tell the joke, I'm laughing, snickering, and slapping my hands on my thighs. By this time, the pictures in my head are so hilarious that I desperately want others to see them too.

The unfortunate fact, though, is when the joke finally does reach the surface, it's not funny to anybody else but me. Apparently, what really *is* funny to everyone is the way I laugh, snort, and carry on.

With all of that said, sometimes silliness and laughter at the right time are good for your heart and soul. The very act of laughing can make you and those around you feel better! Things can get too serious at times, so enjoy the gift of laughter. "A merry heart does good like a medicine" (Proverbs 12:25).

Remember to take good care of yourself. Sometimes you may need to take breaks. Reach out for help so you can get some time for yourself and do the things you need to do to promote and support your own wellness. If your cup is full, you will have so much more to give others. In Chapter 4, we will be looking at how to identify and navigate the important road signs that will occur on this journey, and how to cope and savor the precious moments that lie ahead. You can protect yourself from burnout, stress, and worry by being sure to make the time to take care of *you*. Take naps, take walks, and switch up your routine from time to time to accommodate your needs so you can be the best you can be. And don't forget to keep a sense of humor!

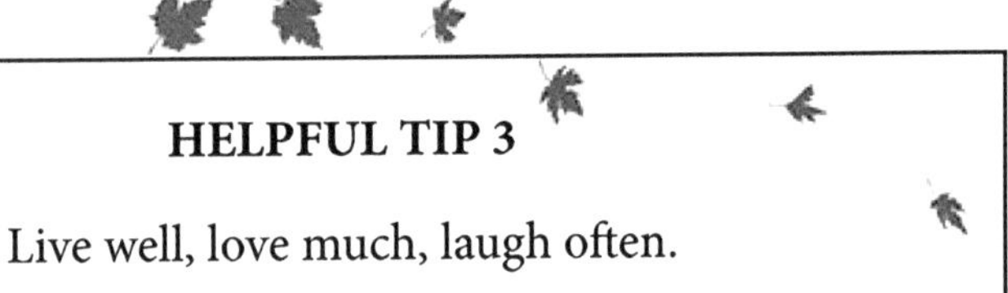

HELPFUL TIP 3

Live well, love much, laugh often.

CHAPTER 4

NAVIGATING THE ROAD SIGNS: WALKING THROUGH THE UNKNOWN

"The ultimate measure of a man is not where he stands in moments of comfort and convenience, but where he stands at times of challenge and controversy."

— Martin Luther King, Jr.

There will be road signs along your journey, benchmarks if you will, for both you and your parent. We all have our own routines and schedules that we are working within, but there will come a time when we will need to interrupt our schedule for our ill parent. We all have obligations, but sometimes things happen, pressing and important things, and we will have to drop everything. Sometimes, they are urgent, and sometimes they are not as urgent as we are told they are. Use a discerning heart. "I'll get there tomorrow" might be too late. Illness and death don't wait; they just happen, so read the road signs properly as they occur and allow them to be your guide to monitoring the horizon ahead. You will need to be flexible in order to be of maximum service to your parent when they need you most. Learning to be flexible helps take some of the stress off of you and your parent. If you have trouble reading the signs, stop to ask for help. This is very wise to do and I so applaud those who do it.

ROLE REVERSAL

When did the role reversal begin and did *you* even notice?

I was twenty-five when the role reversal began between my mother and me, and we both fought it, kicking and screaming. In actuality, I looked calm, cool, and collected, but in my heart, I was rebelling. All I could think was, *It isn't my job to take care of my mother. I am the child here and you're my mom*, even though at the time I was married and pregnant with my second child.

The role reversal event was triggered by my mom's alcoholism; she was going through DTs (delirium tremens) on her own, although I was unaware of this at the time. It was a cold February day when she called and asked me for help. I wasn't quite sure what that meant, so I decided to drive over to her apartment to find out. She lived within a twenty-minute drive, so it wasn't a long ride, but I was definitely feeling a bit anxious and apprehensive about what I might find.

My mom's alcoholism had begun years before, but she didn't display any signs until my early high school years. From that time forward, the tell-tale signs began to be more obvious. From time to time, when she returned home from work, she would smell like alcohol and slur her words. Occasionally, she would come home and become argumentative. Her demeanor was becoming sloppy, and I hated that. I went to bed crying many times. By the time I was a senior in high school, her addiction was apparent, so I wanted to get as far away from it as possible. I could no longer handle the pain or the repulsion and disgust I was feeling toward her, and I was too immature at the time to understand it fully. This was the beginning of the role reversal between my mother and me. When my mother was drinking, I worried so much about her that I became the parent. I felt like *somebody* needed to be in control.

During my college years, my parents had moved two hours to the north of me due to a new job opportunity for my father. The second year after the move, my parents' marriage fell apart and my mom's drinking increased. She managed to keep a steady job, but her life was beginning to unravel. It became very uncomfortable to visit her, and it was difficult to have a normal telephone call with her without noticing the slur in her speech.

Three or four years later, my mom moved back into my part of town. She had sold the big house up north and purchased a mobile home within fifteen minutes of me, my husband, and our four small children. She found work quickly and continued to maintain a forty-hour work week to the best of her ability. She worked as a plant propagator in wholesale plant nurseries. She was born with a green thumb and so enjoyed the solitude of gardening; she could make *anything* grow!

Time moved forward and Mom lost her job. She began physically and emotionally to spiral downward. One thing led to another and things got worse. Holidays turned into bad scenes. She finally had to sell her mobile home and move to an apartment due to poor financial choices. As mom spiraled, so did my heart. It was very rough to watch her decline, especially since I did not know how to "fix" her or the problem.

As a child, I had loved my mom deeply. She and I sang together in the kitchen while doing dishes, we laughed together while watching Elvis Presley movies at all hours, but somehow, at an early age, I learned to worry about her. At times, I can remember worrying about something happening to her to the point of crying and being ill to my stomach. (Boy, was something wrong there.)

Addictions affect the whole family, not just the abuser!

With trepidation after receiving my mother's call for help, I entered my mom's apartment that day and found her very ill. After surveying the room, I realized she had been sleeping on the couch for several days, dishes and old food still resting on the coffee table with old, stale cigarettes smashed into the food and ashtrays. Mom was in her nightgown with a couple of red stains on the back lower portion. I quickly realized how ill she was and that she needed to see a doctor. She, too, knew the severity of the situation, but she was not willing to go *unless* I agreed to shower her first.

Growing up, it wasn't unusual to be in the bathroom at the same time as my mom. We had only one bathroom in the house, so washing your hair in the sink while mom bathed wasn't a big deal, but now as an adult, things felt uncomfortable. I knew then that I needed to push through the discomfort and get her into the shower. The honing of *respect, honor, and dignity* began.

I set to the task of getting my mom undressed and worked hard to get her into the shower. With her in arm's reach and stable, I diligently began to brush my mom's dentures in her bathroom sink as warm and painful tears rolled down my face.

Somehow, deep down inside, my mom still wanted to look *decent* and *presentable* to the doctor. (Go figure!)

In my opinion, her condition at that time didn't dictate an emergency room visit, but after a thorough examination by the doctor, an immediate admission to alcohol rehabilitation was in order. There was no stopping back home to pick up some clothes and a suitcase, just a phone call and a car trip to one of the local community rehab centers for drug and alcohol abuse.... Oh, and a small personal check for $10,000.

LEARNING TO HONOR AND RESPECT

At this point, you may be asking one of the following questions:

- How do I *honor* someone whom I am presently very angry with?
- How do I *honor* someone who doesn't even deserve to be honored?
- How do I *respect* someone who doesn't even respect him- or herself?

Believe me, these were not easy things for me to do, but deep down inside, despite many years of hurt and disappointment, I still loved my mom, but I certainly didn't like her (or her choices). My mom and I had been very close until my parents' marriage went bad *and* her casual drinking turned into an addiction. As a teenager, I never knew or even understood the depth of *her* pain and disappointments. She was very private about her deep feelings, and she felt you should never tell others about your problems, so I guess she drank them away—or at least tried to.

So when her drinking got worse, I began to pull away and lose respect for her and her behavior. After twenty-two years of a marriage going down the tubes, major surgery, and some poor choices, my mom suffered a stroke. By that point, she was renting a bedroom from a random woman fifteen minutes away from me. I was unaware of her location or situation at that time due to her walking out of my life five years before. One more big disappointment, and man, had that been hurtful!

The thing you need to understand is that when I was growing up, my mom was just like June Cleaver on *Leave It to Beaver*. (Hopefully, you can remember that far back.) We weren't wealthy by any means, but my mom was always clean, kept her hair nice, and would dress in a skirt, nylons, and a necklace. She kept a clean house, was a fabulous cook, got up with us kids on school days, packed us lunch, and always remembered our birthdays with a cake at our place at the table that morning. She was a stay-at-home mom and a very hard worker.

The only time my mom wore pants was when she worked outside or in the garden. It wasn't until she was in her late thirties that she began wearing slacks. My father, being a military man, was often gone, so she ran the house, but when he came home, the stress came home with him. Mom was in charge of the inside and the outside of the house, regardless of the season or weather. My father had asthma and many airborne allergies so he stayed clear of all the house and yard work.

My mom was a great cook too. She was born and raised in Germany; hence, hard work, eating well, and having a beer all went together, until it all fell apart, one piece after another. *And my father wasn't a prince either.* I believe my father really drove my mom way beyond herself until she wasn't able to cope anymore. Her physical strength was there, but her emotional strength was spent, so the only way out was to medicate the pain and sorrow, which she did by drinking.

With that all said, *how do you respect and honor* someone like that, after the pity is all gone? A counselor once told me, "How you honor your parents is *for you to live an honorable life.*" That was how I began to learn to show respect and honor toward my mom. As I did, I recognized where and how to give her the dignity she needed. (It may not have always been deserved, but it was needed at times.)

There were small things I could do to honor and show respect to her like combing her hair when she rose from a nap, closing the bathroom door when she was on the commode, helping her into a clean blouse after a snack, and toward the end, helping her change in and out of her disposable panties. She would refer to them as "diapers" like many people do, but I chose to call them panties to keep some dignity in it for her. When your parent gets to the point of needing help bathing and toileting, *extra grace* is required.

LEARNING TO COPE

As I began caring for my mom in her later years, I started noticing small changes in her behavior both mentally and physically. I would sense pain in her face and body as she would rub her shoulder or her upper abdomen, yet she would not give away any evidence that she was experiencing discomfort. I knew my mom well, and at this stage of the game, she would have denied its haunting presence. She was a strong woman in body who never saw the need to burden anyone with her aches and pains, yet I silently took notes.

As the months moved forward, Mom began to limp due to hip and lower back pain. I would watch her frustration trying to pry open jelly jar lids and Tylenol bottles with her thick, bent, arthritic fingers. I could see her disappointment when she could not fit into her favorite shoes anymore due to the swelling in her hands and feet, caused by heart disease and diabetes.

My mom was never a complainer, but as I watched her go about her days, *I began to grieve her losses, both for her and myself.* That was when I began to recognize the road signs of what was yet to come. Take note and start to recognize the mental and physical changes in your parent and be really honest about what you observe, even if it is scary, and even if no one else in the family can see these changes.

Don't try to put the changes in any particular order necessarily; just begin to list the small or big things that come to mind. There's no quiz at the end and no grading, just pure honest observation. However, *don't do this in your parent's presence*. This is an example of when to practice respect, honor, and dignity. Use the lines below to list your observations:

____

____

____

____

____

____

____

____

____

The point here is to unload your observations for now and later return and rate them starting with what you perceive to be your parent's greatest challenge down to the least.

With different seasons of life, one area of concern might be in the "limelight" more so than another, and then out of nowhere, something else comes along and broadsides your parent's health and yours as well. Here's a little saying I always try to keep in the back of my mind:

"Blessed are the flexible for they shall not break."

— Anne Strand

No, it's not a quote from the Bible, but it's worth pondering and heeding.

Keep in mind there will be occasions when you will want to stop and investigate to gain more information about what is happening to your parent, but dwelling too long on the declines won't do anyone any good. As you learn to cope with changes that are occurring in your parent mentally and physically, remember to use kind words and be gentle. Don't be flippant or rude when addressing these changes.

I suggest looking for life's simple pleasures to celebrate with your parent. For example, notice a beautiful sunny day; it's as simple as that. Take a thirty-minute car ride to look at the leaves changing color. Create a stress-free morning by simply sharing together a warm cup of coffee and toast, or a movie afternoon/night at home, or even simply enjoying a piece of your parent's favorite pie with ice cream melting on the top.

Do your best to focus on the good things while being mindful of the road signs you are noticing. Experiencing the simple pleasures and spending quality time with your parent will help you walk through the unknown and cope with the road signs more successfully and with peace in your heart.

TURNING THE CORNER

Sometimes, turning the corner can describe something good, and sometimes, not so much! You are likely to experience some of each: *the good, the bad, and the ugly.* The following story is just one example of one of those times.

It was mid-March 2013 when Larry and I stepped off the cruise ship on a Sunday after seven days of glorious rest and sunshine. Due to an early disembarkation off the ship, and the difficulty finding an affordable return flight back to Seattle for the same morning, we had pre-booked a one-night stay at a nearby hotel where we hoped to get one more day of rest. Within an hour after arriving at our hotel, we found it was naptime.

Just as we were finishing our nap, my cell phone rang. It was 5 p.m. Florida time, on a Sunday afternoon, and the caller was Carol, the hospice nurse, whom we had left in charge of my father-in-law back home in Everett, eight days earlier. She began to tell me of the numerous phone messages she had been receiving from the nursing staff at the SNF where he was now residing. Carol was greatly concerned and so were we.

Little did we know that upon returning home from our cruise, we would be walking into a mess. While we were at sea, my father-in-law had been building up steam and had started acting out in fits of anger in or during our absence. We returned home to stories of him throwing his food and wrapping his oxygen cord around his neck. His disdain for his new (nursing home) residence and toward his life situation exploded like dynamite.

He became paranoid, and it was not a pretty picture! He was fearful that his life was coming to a close, which seemed impossible for him to accept, and he believed a full-blown conspiracy was in progress. He was not only paranoid about the actual nursing home, but also about the workers, the television, and his family, whom he believed wanted to poison him. He was even paranoid about me, his advocate and voice for the past seven years, ever since my mother-in-law had passed away. This was a turn we had not anticipated, and we knew it was a significant road sign for all of us. Sensing we had little time to waste, we began to depend on the assistance and wisdom of the hospice team and nursing staff even more. This was a major turning point.

SAVORING THE MOMENT

Interestingly, some of the most precious moments seem to spring up out of nowhere, but often, we aren't prepared with camera in hand, or we may not have anyone else with us to experience the gift these precious moments bring. Below is just one of many "Kodak moments" I wish I could have recorded.

One late autumn day, I was visiting my friend Opal. She had been a resident at a brand new assisted living facility in Bellevue, Washington, for two years. During this time, I had noticed a sharp decline in her memory. Her family, knowing of our close friendship, had contacted me to see whether I could somehow remind her of some self-care issues that needed attention. They told me Opal seemed to listen to me more than them.

I had noticed on several visits that Opal's clothes didn't seem to change from day to day and that she had more body odor than during prior visits. Also, her bed remained made, no matter what time of day it was. She seemed to lose track of when it was morning or evening or of the date, and she always seemed surprised when I came to visit, even though we had scheduled it weeks earlier. Finally, admitting to myself that she was experiencing some form of dementia, I realized our times together were now going to change.

On this particular visit, Opal asked whether I wanted to meet a friend of hers. She said he was a fellow resident at the nursing home, and at one time, he had lived in an apartment just down the hall from her. I noticed the concern on her face as she added, "And for some unknown reason, his daughter moved him out of his apartment and put him into the secured unit on the lower floor for people with dementia. John doesn't know why and neither do I."

She told me she visited him often and they really enjoyed each other's company. So off we went to the lower floor to visit John. Upon exiting the elevator, we approached another set of closed doors with a keypad, snuggly secured, to the right side of its frame. Above it were operation instructions and the secret code, only backwards. Entering the code correctly unlocked the doors to another world altogether: the memory care unit. *Having a separate unit specific to those with dementia provides safety for those on either side of the doors.*

Once inside, I noticed this floor looked just like the other floors in the building except it was more simplified. Everything else seemed the same. Opal led me down the hall to her friend John's room, and we knocked on his open door.

John was an elderly, tall, trim, and well-dressed gentleman. He said hello, and with a twinkle in her eye, Opal smiled and introduced me to him. John smiled back and then gently shook my hand. He opened the door wide and invited us in. It was a very small apartment, with a living room, bathroom, and small bedroom. There was no kitchen. His place was nicely decorated, including books and photos. My guess was his daughter had done the decorating to help make her father's room a home.

As John motioned for us to sit, he turned to Opal, and in such a polite manner, he asked her name. He said he had forgotten and to please excuse him. They smiled and chatted on as I watched from my chair. It was a fabulous time. Opal and John carried on as if they were old-time friends, although their conversation was very simple and didn't really go anywhere. As the two spoke, Opal would ask the questions and John would answer. In the same polite fashion, he again leaned toward her to ask her name and where they had met.

I watched and listened as if I were far away, even though I was still in the same chair. I drank in their smiles and sweet candor. I silently smiled at the gentle touch of Opal's hand on John's arm, and I felt the joy of friendship flowing between them.

Again, John drew close to Opal and politely asked her name. She smiled and tenderly repeated her name. The story began over and over of how they met. They never missed a beat. It was very touching to watch because I knew the minute we walked out the door, both of them would forget the beauty of what had just happened, except for me.

The time had come when Opal and I needed to leave, so John walked us to his door. He graciously thanked us for the visit and invited us to come again. Before we left his door, he politely asked us our names and how we knew him. That truly was a "Kodak moment." Make savoring the moment a priority. You never know how much time you have. Make sure the time you spend counts.

Over time, navigating the road signs and walking through the unknown will become less daunting. Observe your parent along the way and write down your observations. Don't forget to enjoy the simple pleasures and to allow yourself to be vulnerable. As you experience the good, the bad, and the ugly, be sure to focus on the good. Whether you know how much time you have or whether this knowledge is a mystery, enjoy *your* precious moments.

HELPFUL TIP 4

Remember: Blessed are the flexible for they shall not break.

LOVED ONE, FORGIVE ME AS I AGE

Loved one, forgive me as I age.
Forgive me
For being forgetful about the memories we once shared so sweet.
Forgive me
When my mind isn't clear on the simple things.
Love me through my moodiness and simple frustrations.
Forgive me when I can't move as fast as you, or jump even a small jump.
Laugh with me, not at me.
Smile at me
Now and then, more so now than later.
Give me a squeeze
When I look confused when the answer is right in front of me.
Dine with me
For I am slower than you, and enjoy a lingering hour of leisure.
Forgive me
For when my hair is a mess; my eyes aren't as clear as they used to be.
Spend time with me and listen.
Take notes in your heart
For I am full of explorations and treasures.
But remember, if only you watch with your heart, laugh with your eyes,
and take the time to see,
Can you see me now.

— Sue Stults, 2008

(Written one year prior to my mother's passing)

CHAPTER 5

REALIZING DISAPPOINTMENTS AND FAILURES

"Oh, what a tangled web do parents weave when they think that their children are naive."

— Ogden Nash

Parents want to protect their children, even when they're grown. Many times they won't tell you they've been to the doctor or even the hospital for a quick visit or stay because they don't want to worry or upset you. Your parents know your life is busy with school, work, and family, so they don't want to *bother* you. You may call them or see them now and then, and when you *do* ask how they are, they probably often respond with, "I'm fine." If your parent is over sixty, I would suggest stopping by for a visit more often if you can. Health issues can come on slowly or rapidly, so take a look with your own eyes. You can easily miss important changes that you can't necessarily hear during a phone call. Make it a point to check in regularly on your parent and practice being an intentional listener. Be observant. Do not forget to enjoy the visit, and remember you are not *spying*, but observing.

MEMORY FAILURE

I remember when I became acutely aware that my mother was having memory issues and needed assurance from me that she was okay. One afternoon, she was convinced the woman next-door had come into her apartment and stolen all the coffee in her pantry. What I realized was she had drank all six cans of coffee over the past several months and didn't remember doing so. She always had a couple of extra cans stored there, and now they were all gone. Hmmm....

On a different day, she was convinced the same neighbor had stolen, and was wearing, one of her blouses because she couldn't find it in her closet. She asked me to investigate. Instead of laughing it off or making my mom feel foolish, I honored her request. I just happened to know the next-door neighbor, so I thought I would make a friendly visit. Mom's neighbor was also suffering from ill health, so my strategy was focused on a warm hello and to see how things were going for her.

After two knocks at the front door, the neighbor appeared to greet me. In that instant, I found the answer to my mom's question and concern. The neighbor was not wearing my mom's blouse. I was very sure of that because the missing blouse was one I had purchased for my mom while traveling. The neighbor and I had a great little chat, but I never shared the full reason behind my visit out of respect for my mom. Returning back to mom's apartment, I reassured her she was mistaken about the blouse, and with a heavy sigh, my mom responded; "I think I'm losing it." I replied, "It's okay, Mom. Your secret is safe with me."

Later that day, I suggested we look through her closet to make sure the missing blouse did not get hidden in the back or accidentally fall off its hanger. We finally found it squeezed between some other clothes, and we celebrated! Belittling or humiliating your parent is never a solution. Remember to practice *respect, honor, and dignity.*

Did you know there is a difference between forgetfulness and memory failure/impairment? Everyone experiences temporary forgetfulness from time-to-time that can be exacerbated by stress, or from being overwhelmed. However, memory failure is a permanent decompensation of the brain. Granted, several diseases rob our memory, and many people might not even realize they have memory loss. Even more scary and frustrating, by the time we begin to recognize we can't remember things, it may already be beyond our control. Your parent may fear admitting a memory impairment. Show your parent that you are a safe person to confide in and you will be there to help them through this, whatever it is, and that you are around for the long haul. The lesson here is to learn to have an attitude of ambiguity; your parent may feel they are in uncharted territory, which can be really unsettling.

DEMENTIA

According to the Canadian Alzheimer's Society website, the word "dementia" describes a set of symptoms that may include memory loss and difficulties with thinking, problem-solving, or language. These changes are often small to start with, but for someone with dementia, they have become severe enough to affect daily living. A person with dementia may also experience changes in mood or behavior. Dementia refers to a range of disorders that affect the brain.

Currently, the American Medical Association has identified over sixty-six different forms of dementia; Alzheimer's is just *one* of many. Perhaps you have even heard of some of the others, such as vascular dementia, Lewy body, and, of course, Parkinson's disease.

ALZHEIMER'S DISEASE

For most of us, Alzheimer's is what we think of when we hear the words dementia, memory issues, and forgetfulness. Alzheimer's *is* a disease. It was discovered by Dr. Alzheimer back in 1906. Alzheimer's will eventually diminish a person's life, piece-by-piece. If you and your parents are struggling with the effects of Alzheimer's, take the time to find out all you can. The Alzheimer's Association is a terrific place to start. Educate yourself and your family by attending a workshop or seminar in your community.

A recent article, "Love Your Brain,"[1] by Dr. Heather Snyder states that Alzheimer's is the most common type of dementia, which is a general term for memory loss and the loss of other cognitive abilities severe enough to interfere with daily living. Today 5.5 million Americans are living with this disease. Here are the ten identified Warning Signs of Alzheimer's which the Alzheimer's Organization

1 *The Costco Connection Magazine*. June 2017. p. 69.

posts on its website:

1. Confusion with time or place
2. Memory loss that disturbs daily living
3. Challenges in planning or solving problems
4. Difficulty completing familiar tasks at home, at work, or at leisure
5. Trouble with understanding visual images or spatial relationships
6. New problems with words in speaking or writing
7. Misplacing things and losing the ability to retrace steps
8. Decreased or poor judgment
9. Withdrawal from work or social activities
10. Changes in mood and personality

Also, the Alzheimer's Association recommends consulting a doctor if you notice any of these signs. If you are concerned about your parent's memory, take them to see their primary physician or find a good geriatric physician to evaluate them. As your parent's memory begins to wane and their short-term recall diminishes, you will find them leaning on *your* memory more frequently to aid them. While this may take some getting used to on your part, don't forget: *respect, honor, and dignity.*

If you begin experiencing frustration and impatience over your parent's lack of memory, which is common, don't belittle them by gasping, snorting, or rolling your eyes because they can't remember. Instead, take a deep breath, put on your big boy pants, and gracefully step forward to help. Many times, your parent is more frustrated and embarrassed about their loss of memory than you are. Think about those times (which we all have had at one time or another) when our *own* minds draw a blank or we experience a *mental hiccup* if you will. It can be most embarrassing, especially when you are introducing your closest friend to someone new (been there, done that). Imagine what it must be like for your parent who taught you to walk and talk and now can't even remember your name anymore!

Several years ago, I had the privilege of meeting a woman named Teepa Snow. Teepa is an amazing speaker, communicator, and dementia educator, who specializes in the field of geriatrics. I had the joy of sharing the speaking platform with her three years in a row at a large annual Care Conference in Shoreline, Washington.

I felt inspired to create an inclusive care conference that would infuse the crowd with much needed education and information on caring for an aging parent and dementia. With the hard work and support of my church, Shoreline Community Church, its Care Team, and friends, the annual Care Conference was born! Each year brought increasing attendance, topping off at three hundred registered attendees! People are hungry for information.

Even as I am writing this book, I am receiving telephone calls inquiring when the next Care Conference is scheduled. My intention for each conference is to educate and equip the audience with *The Personal Health Care Manual* and teach them how to use it properly. Each year, I speak about being an advocate and leader of the family, and I close with the topic of hospice and describe what great work it does. I speak about tough topics and start the difficult conversations people don't want to have, such as about hospice and end-of-life issues.

At our last event, when the microphone was turned over to Teepa

Snow, the crowd drew close. Many attendees had come to learn specifically about dementia and Alzheimer's. These diseases are no longer thought of as solely elderly adult issues. Onset can happen as early as age thirty-five. Teepa explained how the disease affects the brain and presents itself in the actions/behavior (or lack of) in a person. She provided role-play scenarios that helped the audience members internalize important information so they could identify symptoms in their loved ones and know how to work with the changes; she taught how to do the "dance."

Here is just one of the many positive comments received from our attendees:

> Until I attended the first Care Conference in October, I had no idea what dementia "looked like." I found myself reacting with irritation and impatience to what I felt was unreasonable behavior. This certainly strained my relationship with my husband as well as challenged my Christian convictions. The understanding came in the form of the Shoreline Community Church Care Conference through the *powerful* information shared by both speakers Sue Stults and Teepa Snow. Talk about telling it like it *really* is!
>
> I not only came to realize that I was not the only person struggling with this challenge, I also felt the support from both the leadership and the other men and women in attendance. *It felt like a warm hug in the midst of the storm.*

In the next fifteen years, Alzheimer's is estimated to increase by 50 percent! Dementia is no respecter of person or age anymore. Educate yourself on the illness, disease, and diagnosis of the health issues surrounding your parent. Doing so will help you better understand how things will progress and where their health issues may lead. You don't need to over-study. Being aware of the progression of your parent's illness and how best to manage it are the most important elements of their care and, equally important, is your responsibility to ensure they are not a danger to themselves or others. In the next section, we will address a major area of concern: driving a motor vehicle.

TAKING THE CAR KEYS AWAY

For many of us independent souls, the thought of depending on someone else for transportation is earthshaking. The fear of losing our independence is enormous. In many ways, it's the beginning of the end, and that's why there's usually a fight to give up the car keys.

One day, prior to surrendering her car keys, my mom called me because she had locked her car keys inside her car with the engine still running. Thankfully, I had a spare set of keys at the time and lived only a few minutes away.

Another sign that my mom was no longer safe on the road was when one of my children needed a ride home after school and I had phoned her to help me out. She loved her grandchildren, and this was just another way for her to spend a little one-on-one time with one of them, so she agreed to help out by picking up my son. Returning home that day, my son revealed that my mother was hesitating at green lights and proceeding through red lights. At first I thought my son was just stretching the truth a bit, but when I heard she had mistakenly passed our driveway and backed up (on a main arterial) to get to it, I was horrified!

What else was happening while she was driving that I did not know about? I realized it was time to take some action, but *what*, or even *how*? I struggled with the fact that I was *her* child (thirty-eight and a mother of four), so what right did I have to step in and take her car keys away? When is it an appropriate time to take the keys away?

This is a great question with many possible solutions. Let's take a look at some of them. Most of us hope the time will never come when we, as adult children, have to take the cars keys away from our parent. The scenarios are many, but the solution is limited to one:

You must take the keys away for their safety and yours!

I was ever so grateful the day my mom finally decided to stop driving and handed over the keys. She came to realize she wasn't feeling safe driving anymore. At that point in time, we were all concerned about her driving, but we weren't brave enough to do something about it. Some of you may be able just to march right in and take those keys away the minute you suspect your parent is no longer able to drive safely, but not all of us can.

Sometime later, after the deed of removing the keys is over, the truth comes out and the untold "car stories" begin to emerge: the close calls, forgetting how to get back home, or the lost car at the mall or grocery store that security had to help your parent find. Chances are, if you or your parent are noticing that their driving is impaired, or they are having difficulty navigating their environment when driving, it may be time to make some difficult decisions, not driving being one of them.

You may be asking yourself, *What are the signs I should be noticing?* First, I would suggest listening to your parent as they talk about their day and activities. You will learn a lot about them and their struggles and frustrations by just lending an ear. Keep in mind that numerous things can hinder your parent's driving skills.

Health issues such as vision loss, stroke, hearing loss, dementia, and even medication can alter their ability to drive safely. Aging itself can be a component in driving safely because reaction time for elders is much slower. With that in mind, take everything into consideration before you make the decision to remove the car keys from your parent. Following are some suggestions I would recommend trying when you are contemplating taking those car keys away.

First, select an appropriate time, when your parent is calm, to approach them with your concerns about their driving. Be mindful of the *respect, honor, and dignity* rule. Speak in a normal tone of voice and be sure to have their attention. Begin the conversation with something like, "So, Dad/Mom, I noticed you have a ding in your bumper. What happened?" Listen carefully to their reply and then maybe comment like "Oh, wow!" or "That's too bad."

Remember, *no scolding*. Let your parent tell the story so you can understand what happened through their eyes. Let *them* paint the picture so you can see. Then you can continue the conversation with something more, for example, "Well, you know I've been concerned about your driving lately. Are *you* feeling safe out there?" Or "Is it getting a little harder these days for you to drive?" Here's where you *listen*. Then interject something like: "Well, I would really like you and all the other people out there to be safe, so I think it might be time for you to stop driving. I understand it's a *huge* thing to give up, and you're probably feeling like you're losing your independence, but I can help you figure it out." If it comes to the point where you have reasoned with your parent and they *still* will not surrender the keys, you may want to try one of these other suggestions:

- Have a confidential phone conversation with your parent's doctor. Share your concerns about your parent's driving. Suggest the doctor's office call and set up a "well check-up" or "medication check back" appointment so the doctor can see your parent face to face and then gently inform your parent that he or she cannot be driving anymore. If possible, attend the appointment with your parent.
- Contact the Department of Licensing and inform them of your concern. Your parent will receive a letter in the mail stating they will most likely have to retake the driving test again.
- Hide the car keys or just remove them from the house. *Do not* give the other parent the keys if they are not driving themselves anymore. This will surely raise havoc in their home.
- Disconnect the battery cable/starter. And, finally, if all else fails:
- *Remove* the car completely. This final step can really cause a lot of anger in a parent and may create a strained relationship, so use this one as the last resort, if possible.

You will need to make tough and sometimes painful decisions for your parent. Remember that you must take responsibility for your parent's safety, which must be the top priority at all times.

HELPFUL TIP 5

Remember, you are responsible for your parent's safety; that must be the top priority at all times.

CHAPTER 6

BECOMING AN ADVOCATE

"And the truth of the matter is, we all
come with an expiration date."

— Author Unknown

It is a dose of reality to recognize and accept that there will come a time when caring for someone else becomes all about them. Surprise! It's not about *you* anymore. It is so important that you hear me when I say this so I will repeat it: *It's not about you anymore!* That's right. Let me explain. It doesn't mean you aren't needed anymore or that you aren't important to your parent. On the contrary, you are now needed more than ever.

Certain realities we cannot avoid no matter how hard we try, and the truth is that we all come with an expiration date. Many people fear the thought of dying, but in actuality, what brings us the most fear is the process we might have to travel through to come to the very end. Will there be pain and suffering, and who will take care of us in the end? These are pointed questions we have to consider.

THE REALITY

For one person, death will be due to cancer, and for another, leukemia, AIDS, heart disease, diabetes, kidney failure, or a fall with a broken hip that turns into pneumonia. Regardless of how we die, death will eventually take our breath away. Our bodies are like fine-tuned machines, but we are not designed to live in our mortal bodies forever, and they *do* eventually begin to wear out. The washers and cogs begin to wear out in our knees and hips, and our rotator cuffs and eyes follow. And while we may be in total disbelief, somehow, out of nowhere, our hair starts to sprout with new life somewhere else on our bodies. (We really *are* wonderfully and fearfully made.) As our physical strength and stamina diminishes, our mental abilities are making changes as well.

In many cases, the ability to have a conversation in a crowd may become difficult or overwhelming. More concentration may be needed when following directions, or loud noises and activity around us may become a source of irritation. For some people, in particular, these things can really wear them out. Difficulty hearing occurs for many people in their later years, and unless you are aware of this, you may find yourself in a very frustrating situation.

Here are some simple suggestions to try with your parent sometime. The key here is *not* letting your parent know you are monitoring their ability to hear. Next time you are engaged in a conversation with them:

- Turn your head as you are talking as though you are looking at something in the room and keep talking. Next, return back to face your parent. Did they hear you?
- Begin talking normally to your parent upon entering the room and continue as you would normally do on a visit, checking to see whether they are following the conversation.
- Periodically find a reason to turn your back on them during a conversation and ask them a question. Were they able to answer the question?
- Lastly, try talking with your hand by your chin, hiding your mouth just a bit. Were they still engaged in the conversation? Could they hear you, even though they did not see your mouth moving?

These simple tests are a barometer and can be done at anytime, anywhere. Your findings will help you determine whether there may be a hearing problem or a comprehension issue, or maybe something else is going on.

Hearing aids and eyeglasses can help if your parent's hearing or vision begins to fail, but what happens when you don't know what the "something else" is? Could it be a physiological problem or a cognitive issue? Whatever it is, this is the time to investigate and begin looking for answers.

LEARNING NEW TERMINOLOGY

When I first began walking with my dad through his terminal lung cancer, I found myself lost in a new language when it came to his medical care and the surrounding issues. It was important for me to learn new terminology so I could understand what was being said and so I could be clear about the indications of what was going on. I have compiled a small glossary of key words for you, possibly new words, which you might encounter in the process of taking care of your parents. Take a look below to see whether any of these terms may already be familiar:

ADLs: Activities of Daily Living.

Adult Day Care: A private pay day care center for physically or mentally impaired adults.

Adult Family Home: A privately owned and operated home that provides a family atmosphere with specially trained staff. Private pay with possible state assistance.

Artificial Nutrition and Hydration: Food and fluids provided through a device such as a tube or intravenous catheter so a patient is not required to chew or swallow voluntarily. Artificial nutrition and hydration does not include assisted feeding such as spoon or bottle-feeding.

Assets: 1) Property owned by a particular person or organization; 2) Property of a person that can be taken by law for the settlement of debts or that forms part of a deceased person's estate.

Assisted Living: Live-in community that promotes independent living and includes 1-3 meals a day with assistance if needed. Apartment style living.

Custodial Care: Assistance with the activities of daily living usually on a long-term basis, provided to people who are unable to take care of themselves.

CPR (Cardiopulmonary Resuscitation): A process that keeps the heart pumping and provides oxygen to the blood through artificial means.

DNR/DNAR: Do not resuscitate/Do not attempt resuscitation.

Hospice: Assigned only by a doctor. Specialty care for advanced illness with life expectancy of six months or less. Comfort care only.

LPN: Licensed practical nurse.

Medicaid: Program funded by the US and state governments that pays the medical expenses of people unable to pay some or all of their own expenses.

Medicare: Health insurance program in the United States under which medical care and hospital treatment for people sixty-five or older is partially paid by the government.

Nurse Practitioner (ARNP): Registered nurse trained in primary health care to assume certain responsibilities once assumed only by a physician, such as the diagnosis and treatment of minor illnesses.

Palliative Care: Directed at providing comfort care rather than curative care.

POA (Power of Attorney): Legal authority to act on behalf of another.

POLST: Physician's order of life-sustaining treatment. Hard brightly colored form that states end of life choices pre-discussed with patient and doctor. Doctor signature needed. (The color varies from state to state in the United States.)

RN: Registered nurse.

SNF (Skilled Nursing Facility): Also known as nursing homes or rehabilitation facilities. These offer the highest level of care by providing nurses and other professionals with specialized skills, i.e., wound care, IV therapy, and physical/occupational therapy, etc.

Spend Down: Seniors and people with disabilities whose incomes exceed the income limit may qualify for Medicaid if they have medical bills that equal or are greater than their "excess" income. The process of subtracting those medical bills from the individual's income over a six-month period is called a Medicaid "spend down."

Supplemental Insurance: Any form of insurance in addition to Medicare coverage.

I hope this list of key words helps you begin to understand some common terms used by the medical, insurance, and care facilities. Caring for your parent or a loved one really *is* a dose of reality! Don't forget to seek wise counsel, especially when you're not sure how to handle tough situations. Lean on your family and friends for support. When you need to, seek legal counsel and remember to stay open-minded so you can begin to learn important terminology to help you make clearer decisions. In the next chapter, we will talk in-depth about involving family and friends in your parent's care.

UNDERSTANDING THE DIAGNOSIS AND DISEASE

Now that you have gained some knowledge and hopefully educated yourself a bit about your parent and their reality, the next step is to share this information with the people who need to know, including the family. Understanding the diagnosis and disease (even if it's purely aging), will help you in making better decisions about your parent's future. After the initial shock of bad news, a sense of numbness can usually follow. This shock wave and numbness could last minutes, days, or possibly weeks, and your parent is walking through it just like you. Keep in mind as others receive the news that their responses might not be the same as yours.

Everyone will deal with a medical diagnosis in his or her own way. Expect every type of reaction possible so *you won't be caught off guard.* Reactions may include tears, laughter, anger, rage, and possibly silence. Don't be surprised. *Just let it happen*, and let everyone, *even you*, feel it, walk in it, and even taste it. Then in a few days, pick up and move forward because your parent is going to need you to help them through it.

EDUCATION

If anyone lacks wisdom, let them ask. Start asking questions and educating yourself. I'm not suggesting college courses, but I am suggesting lectures, seminars, workshops, books, etc. Do whatever you can to educate yourself to help your parent. Wouldn't you want to know that the people who are being your voice and handling your affairs have some idea of what they are doing? Of course, we all would.

Though there may be limited time when the caregiving becomes more demanding, remember to rotate your family members to help ensure everyone gets a healthy break if possible. Sharing the load will allow everyone to have one-on-one time with your parent before their voice may be completely gone. Have no regrets.

Educating yourself just a bit about the illness, disease, and diagnosis of the health issues surrounding your parent will, in turn, help you understand how things will progress and where these health issues may eventually lead. You don't need to over-study, but being aware of the issues and how to help manage them is important.

As your parent ages, new health issues may arise, so it is important to keep your family/team informed. This, again, will help keep the lines of communication open, which will encourage your parent to be forthright with everything.

Remind your parent that they still have their privacy, but help them *not* to place you in the middle of sibling quarrels, rivalries, or "he said, she said" squabbles. Encourage your parent to speak to the family member directly and in private to clear the air should any upsetting communication occur. Also, try to remind them to avoid the "snowball effect" of unhealthy communication because it takes away valuable time and energy.

Everyone can use an advocate—someone in his or her corner; someone who is willing to learn and become the voice of reason. Become that advocate for your parent or loved one.

MICHELLE'S STORY

A story I like to share to illustrate the importance of having an advocate is about Kenny and Michelle, a young couple who were planning to get married. While Kenny lay ill in the local hospital, his fiancée Michelle sat, stewed, and even brewed over the situation. Unable to jump in a car and rush to his side, she stayed put and waited for the latest news. Was there a new diagnosis, or was it the same bad news about Kenny's ongoing health conditions?

The longer Michelle sat and waited for news, the more she felt helpless, stifled, and stuck. *What can I do for my future husband whom I adore, and how can I aid him again through another dark and scary place?* thought Michelle.

It took some time and effort, but Michelle began to find her help. She started by calling her girlfriends, who were her main source of support. She had already learned to create a support group without being consciously aware of it, and it was already established. She knew whom to call and how to get results. If she couldn't be there at Kenny's bedside, she was going to send someone to be her eyes, ears, and hands to be there.

You see, Michelle was wheelchair bound with cerebral palsy, just like her sweet love Kenny was. She had been in training to be the advocate for her man as a result of her meetings with me. She desperately wanted to learn how to be an advocate, a voice for him. "Teach me," she would say to me. "I want to learn. I want to help my guy."

With fingers curled to her palms and hands postured as fists, even her inability to push elevator buttons at the hospital made it nearly impossible for her to visit. At times, she sat in her motorized wheelchair at the elevator door just waiting for someone to come by to push the buttons. Her heart was there, but her physical ability was limited. Nevertheless, her determination was powerful. What a sweetheart! What a champion!

HELPFUL TIP 6

Learn all you can about your parent's diagnosis and its associated terminology. You can use my helpful *The Personal Health Care Manual* to refresh your memory of the new terminology and to document important developments in your parent's diagnosis and health.

CHAPTER 7

MEETING THE SOCIAL WORKER

"When you don't know what to do, count on someone who does."

— Robin O'Grady

Are you aware that every hospital and nursing home has at least one and often several social workers on staff? (Keep in mind the numbers increase depending upon the facility's size.) If you've ever been in the Emergency Room or stayed in the hospital, you've probably encountered a social worker. Most people rarely remember meeting them due to the stress of the crisis that brought them into the hospital in the first place. The scenario goes something like this:

THE PHONE CALL

It's 1:30 a.m. when the phone rings. You awake with a start, not quite sure where you are and what time it is. All you know is it's still pretty dark outside. You reach for the phone as your stomach and brain sense something is wrong somewhere, and you begin to feel fear in your heart and in the pit of your stomach. As you mumble the word "Hello?" you hear the voice of your parent on the other end. Now you *know* something is wrong, so you throw on your clothes to rush to their side. The car feels cold and so do you. Your mind races to try to think of the possibilities that may present themselves when you arrive. Unbeknownst to you, your adrenal glands are very hard at work. The hormone "adrenaline" is shooting through your veins, giving you extra energy, and you feel ultra-alert.

The body is designed to respond this way. This is the state of "fight or flight" that you have probably heard and read about.

FIGHT-OR-FLIGHT RESPONSE

The fight-or-flight response is an automatic response of the human body, and it is completely out of your control. It is basic to all human nature. It is the physical response to stress.

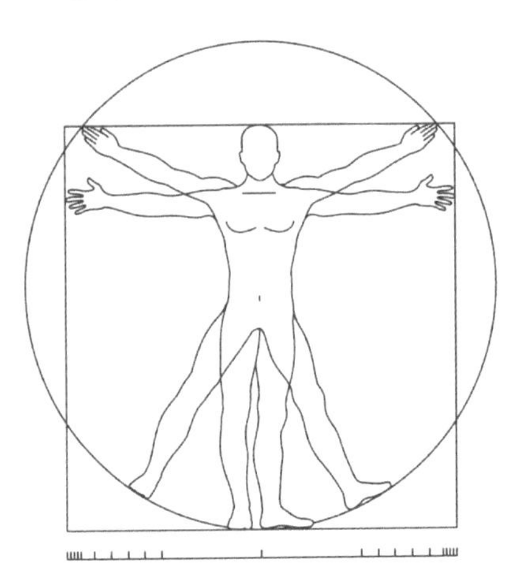

Let me give you a better understanding of what happens inside your body when the fight-or-flight response is activated and how it relates to fear and stress. The fight-or-flight response is triggered by the adrenal gland and the hormone secreted by this gland. The adrenal gland is, according to the *American Heritage Dictionary*, "either of two small, dissimilarly shaped endocrine glands, one located above each kidney, consisting of the cortex, which secretes several steroid hormones, and the medulla, which secretes epinephrine (also epinephrin). It is also called suprarenal gland. Epinephrine is "a hormone secreted by the adrenal medulla that is also called adrenaline. It is also a white to brownish crystalline compound, C 9H 13NO 3, isolated from the adrenal glands of certain mammals or synthesized and used in medicine as a heart stimulant, vasoconstrictor, and bronchial relaxant." As the body works the way it was designed to, the heart is pumping blood to your upper thighs, upper body, and arms to give you the ability to move faster and react more quickly.

When the fight-or-flight response is activated by either a real or perceived danger, the chemicals released will produce some changes in our physical bodies. The large muscles of the upper and lower body will enlarge due to increased blood flow. This prepares us to either fight or take a flight. Obviously, if we were to fight, having additional strength in our upper torso would be advantageous. Likewise, if we were going to flee (flight), having additional strength in our hips and legs would be helpful. But, since the body only has a certain amount of blood to facilitate, these areas require that other areas experience a reduction in blood flow. Some of the changes are:

- Our respiratory rate increases
- Blood flow is redirected to large muscles
- Pupils dilate, which enhances vision
- Cognitive ability goes down
- Digestion stops. Because digestion stops, consider the effect upon the stomach. If there is undigested food in the stomach, the reduced blood flow, which aids in digestion, causes the stomach to become upset. The starch and sugar in the undigested stomach will cause indigestion and nausea.

Other symptoms to be aware of:

- Shock
- Nausea
- Sleep Disturbances
- Sexual Dysfunction
- Problems with Authority Figures
- Time Distortion
- Hyperventilating
- Withdrawal
- Suicidal Thoughts
- Cynicism

You finally arrive at your parent's side. You assess the situation and see your parent needs to go to the hospital. Now you must decide whether to call 911 or drive them in yourself. After that decision is made, you now find yourself in the ER. There, in a small room, you are seated next to your parent, who is now wearing a hospital gown. *As you reach beyond the rail* of the bed to offer comfort, you may find you, too, are in need of some comforting. It's amazing how comforting an unspoken word or just the tenderness of a warm hand can be. *Never* underestimate that.

As the aides and nurses bustle throughout the room, a face from registration appears, clipboard in hand, with papers needing to be signed. The rights and regulations are all printed in fine lettering and are too small to read at length at this time of the morning. Someone is now asking questions regarding your parent's current medications, doctor visits, medical history, and living wills. You find yourself answering questions for your parent. Now is when you realize whether or not you're prepared.

THE SOCIAL WORKER'S ROLE

As the room quiets, the staff is busy in the hall and you find yourself lost in thought. This is just about the time the social worker appears. She (or he) is usually quiet and unobtrusive. She enters the room with only a business card in hand and softly introduces herself: "Hi. My name is Sarah Michaels. I'm the social worker here." She hands you her card and closes the short, stunted conversation with, "If I can be of any help, please let me know." And then she leaves just as quickly as she came.

At this point, you either leave the card on the side table or you slide it into your pocket, really not too sure *who she was* and what she was all about. Your mind is so preoccupied with your parent and what the day may hold that whoever that person or whatever she was selling, you aren't interested.

The doctor finally steps in around the curtain to greet your parent and the tests begin. The morning crawls by, and next thing you know, it's noon and the sun's been up for hours. At this point, your parent is either under observation, admitted to the hospital, or sent home.

That small little card from the social worker has managed to disappear, and you, not being aware of what it had to offer, don't know what it meant anyway in light of the situation at hand. The sting of the early morning phone call is still resonating throughout your body, but now the numbness and exhaustion are beginning to set in.

The adrenaline is wearing off, and that's why you feel so weary. Your fight-or-flight response has served its purpose and helped you to push through for now, but what about next time? Times like these are great examples of when the practice of self-care is necessary but unlikely because you are focused on someone else.

Having a good support system around you is very important. It's a huge part of self-care as we discussed in Chapter 3. Having a sounding board, a shoulder to cry on, and wise counsel are so needed to help you along your journey. A family member, professional counselor, or good friend can be someone who may be able to provide you with all of these things and be an additional source of support. Keep your ears open because your friends love you. They have helpful advice and wise counsel when you need it most.

Seek out the social worker at the hospital or in the skilled nursing/rehabilitation facility within the first day or two of your parent's admission. Social workers can be very busy people, and the demands upon them are high, so make yourself available to them. You can request to speak with a social worker at the nurse's station. Let the social worker know a window of time when you will be available for a call, or ask whether she would kindly stop-in on a predetermined date and time while you are there visiting your parent.

Many people have preconceived ideas that social workers are the ones who come to take your children away, but the truth is that the job of a social worker is huge. In a hospital and in skilled nursing facilities, he or she is literally the kingpin for the care coordination and placement of your parent. Social workers provide resources for families, individuals, groups, and communities in an effort to enhance social functioning and overall wellbeing. Though they are usually in the background and rarely seen, they are always working. One of a social worker's major tasks in hospitals and skilled nursing facilities is to determine what type of coverage and benefits your parent has through their health insurance. They are very aware of insurance companies' rules and regulations, including Medicare and Medicaid and how each works. Be sure to seek out the social worker and share any questions or concerns you have because he or she is there to help you.

HELPFUL TIP 7

Connect with the social worker as soon as possible. He or she will provide valuable information and resources and will be responsible for the care coordination of your parent, including hospital discharge planning.

CHAPTER 8

ESSENTIAL LEGAL DOCUMENTS

"Ethics is knowing the difference between what you have a right to do and what is right to do."

— Potter Stewart

This chapter is critical! You might be thinking your parents are not yet in need of a Will, Living Will, Power Of Attorney, or a POLST form. It may appear to you that it would be a major endeavor and very costly to create these documents, so you may be inclined to hold off on legal matters until things get a bit worse for your parent before you schedule an appointment with an attorney.

This is wrong. Do not wait! Now is the exact time to become prepared and help prepare *them*. You likely purchased this book because some issues were already beginning to show up with your mom and dad and you were looking for guidance, so here it is.

Some illnesses are short term. Recovery happens and life returns to normal. Other illnesses last a few years and bring on permanent life changes, but a new normal is found and life continues. In some cases, however, fatal illnesses occur that eventually cause end of life, so the family will need to learn how to adapt and adjust. This process will require a lot of love, patience, and understanding for everyone involved.

In this journey of caring for your parent, you will find that, at certain segments along the way, you will need to seek good and wise counsel. I encourage you to seek it out and not to presume you know all the answers. A conversation with an accountant, legal advisor, and any other professional in regard to your parent's welfare is *well* worth the time and money spent to get correct answers. Write out your questions before your appointment, and be sure to take good notes.

Some important documents will also need to be signed and financial matters addressed. The more you can accomplish *while your parent has a voice* and a say in their personal affairs, the better.

The way you handle your parent's legal issues and final directives will be determined by the way your parents are handling *their* emotional and physical issues. To expound a bit here, if your parent is in denial or angry and unwilling to discuss the matters they are facing, it can present problems and frustrations for you and the family. Proceed gently with *respect, honor, and dignity*. Things can get accomplished many times easier with these words in mind. You can be firm but respectful at the same time.

POWER OF ATTORNEY

A question I am frequently asked is: When does the Power of Attorney take effect? The type of power given by the signed document will determine the effective date. Most powers of attorney do not go into effect or come into the forefront until your parent is deemed unable to act on their behalf. *At this point, legal counsel is worth the time and money.* If your parent already has an attorney and you feel comfortable and confident with him or her, consult with that attorney. He or she may even have copies of some of the legal documents you will need down the road. If there are no legal documents already put in place by your parent (unfortunately, this is common), such as Power of Attorney for HealthCare, Power of Attorney for Finances, Durable Power of Attorney, Living Will, or Last Will and Testament, *now* is the time to find an attorney and get those items completed. Time does not wait for anyone, and neither does illness or disease.

Seriously, no one really wants to think of their mortality, but I applaud all of those who already *have* their ducks in a row and their legal documents in order before things begin to fall apart. When illness or disease occur, it's rather late in the game of life to get these important things completed, and the stress and pressure is put on the shoulders of the surviving spouse, partner, child, friend, or distant relative.

Always remember this: Whenever there's a crisis or trauma, your brain goes out the window. Therefore, it's best to proceed with caution where legal and medical matters are concerned. Don't be afraid to begin the conversation with your parent about legal issues and final directives. Let your parent know your concern is to make sure their plans and wishes will be carried out and to avoid any confusion regarding their care and affairs. Getting legal affairs in order also serves as protection for any siblings and other relatives who want to step into the picture. The more that is spelled out clearly in legal documents, the better because hearsay is not legally binding.

Sometimes, family members don't want to talk about illness, hospitals, or end-of-life issues, but someone has to start the conversation. If your parent is capable of taking the time to share their wishes and desires with your family, they *empower* their family to act on their behalf.

Did you know, that Federal Law (the Patient Self-Determination Act) states that you, the patient, have the right to: Receive care *or* refuse care.

If at any time you are unable to communicate or are mentally unable to share your wishes, the following documents will let your voice be heard. These documents are referred to as Advance Directives:

- Durable Power of Attorney for Health Care
- Living Will
- DNR/DNAR
- Health Care Directive
- POLST Form
- Five Wishes (Optional)

When these documents are *not* in place, a family member, or legal guardian will be appointed to make the decisions for you, and those decisions may not reflect your true wishes.

Be sure to consult with a legal professional since each state and country may vary in its requirements and legalities.

By taking charge of the situation and helping your parent complete the above documents, you have helped them become proactive and set the stage for their final departure. *Their voice matters! Your action is required!*

If you have already purchased *The Personal Heath Care Manual*, now would be a great time to make copies of your parent's documents and insert them in Section 5, under Advance Directives. If you haven't yet purchased a copy of the manual and would like one, please refer to the Contact Information page in the back of this book. You may contact me by email, go to my website, or reach me directly by phone. I also offer a complimentary thirty-minute consultation. I encourage you to contact me and I will welcome your phone call. I would enjoy hearing from you and helping to answer important questions you may have.

You may be surprised to learn your parent already took care of many of these documents years ago and what a great thing that is. But don't be surprised and don't ridicule them if you find they have nothing in place at all. Much time and energy, and even your relationship, can be lost if you get caught up in their lack of preparation so *don't* even go there. One more time, remember: *respect, honor, and dignity*. Keep in mind that we all have our own style of being organized and keeping office at home, and very seldom is it the same for everyone, so *it is what it is*. Accept it and move on. Choose to love anyway.

This may be another time when reaching out for family support is needed. Then, if necessary, hire a good lawyer to get the proper documents in place.

Let me just say this: Even you may think your family gets along well, which is great, but I have seen way too often that as end of life approaches, things get weird! I kid you not. The most important thing is to get your parent's legal documents in order and put them somewhere safe that you'll remember. (As a side note, be prudent and do the same for yourself by informing your immediate family about some of those important papers and their whereabouts in the event of an emergency. It's never too early to prepare.) If the documents are located in a safety deposit box, make sure you are a signer on the box and know where the bank and key are located. Be sure to bring identification with you. If you are not a signer or your parent passes away, you will need a Power of Attorney or a death certificate to open the box. Plan ahead.

The last piece of information you need to know is to *review your documents every three to five years* to keep them current. Though it may sound foolish to review them this often, you will be surprised by how much may have changed in your parent's life in such a short time. It recently dawned on me that it was time to review our family's legal documents, and I found to my surprise that we still had a guardian in place for our four children who are now *grown adults* and able to care for themselves. Oops! So, *do* take the time to revisit important legal documents with your parent and do the same for your own personal documents. *It's never too early for a review, but it can be too late if you wait too long.*

THE POLST FORM

What is the POLST form and why is it needed? The word POLST is actually an acronym for "Physicians Order of Life Sustaining Treatment." This form is akin to a living will. Make sure you understand the difference between a living will and a last will and testament. A living will, also known as an "advance directive," comes into play only when an individual faces life-threatening conditions and is unable to communicate their desires *for* or *against* specified medical treatment. Depending on the state of residency, a "health care proxy" may be an option. A Last Will and Testament is specific to the personal assets and possessions of an individual and how and to whom they will be dispersed upon his or her death.

Be aware that not every US state or country uses these forms, and in some cases, just the living will or do not resuscitate directives may be satisfactory.

You can be prepared by using the correct and updated forms and documents in the state where your parent currently resides.

In Washington State, the POLST form is printed on hard stock paper and comes in a bright lime green color. In some cases, I have also seen them in bright orange. They are created in bright shades to be seen more easily. It is recommended that you tape this form on the door of the refrigerator, the inside of the front door to the house, and/or even the inside door of the bedroom. This recommendation is because at the time of an emergency, services such as the Fire Department are called, and the workers have been trained to locate these forms in the given locations in an effort to honor the written requests of your parent and to follow proper procedures and protocol.

FIVE WISHES

Five Wishes is an optional and alternative document to what is typically thought of as an advance directive. Once it has been completed and notarized, it constitutes a legal document. The Five Wishes document was created by The Robert Wood Johnson Foundation, and it provides valuable information such as your parent's medical treatment options and preferences. This document will also provide answers to what type of comfort measures your parent is requesting at the end of life.

The Five Wishes is not a necessary document to have, but it is another wonderful tool to add to your toolbox. To find out more about the Five Wishes and receive a copy, visit www.agingwithdignity.org.

YOUR PARENT'S RIGHTS

Never forget that your parent has significant and important rights. Your parent has the right to:

1. Be treated with care.
2. Be handled gently and with decency.
3. Be clean, dry, and fed.
4. Be held and loved.
5. Sleep when they desire; or stay in bed all day if they choose.
6. Eat or even stop eating.
7. Smoke, drink, and do drugs.
8. Take care of themselves or not.
9. And finally, *just stop trying.*

Your parent has the right to their *own* opinion, to make their *own* decisions regarding their money, car, last will and testament, living will, surgery, and medication, even if it means not doing a thing. Again, keep in mind some of these decisions are good, and some are unhealthy and can be downright bad, but *your* role and *your* task is all about: *respect, honor, and dignity*. I encourage you to use the Serenity Prayer below when times get tough to keep your mind and attitude in its proper place. It helped me so many times to keep my head on straight.

God, grant me the serenity
To accept the things I cannot change,
Courage to change the things I can,
And wisdom to know the difference.

— Reinhold Niebuhr

Many have heard the Serenity Prayer before, but if this is the first time for you, don't just close the book and forget about it. Instead, give it a try. It's a good prayer to return to, especially when your journey to care for your parent gets rough, which it will. Walking through this journey with both my mom and dad was a hard and difficult road, and many times I found myself tired and weary.

Returning home to care for a parent after not living with them for a number of years can be very difficult. "The same roof," my father would say, "doesn't always look the same the second time around." Your eyes and ears are coping with new sights, and sometimes, new smells. Perhaps your personal values are pushed to the limits or have changed, or habits and behaviors that you were not aware of are now evident. There may even be some illegal behavior or activity taking place. *Please hear me out here because this is of great importance!*

Pain (mental or physical) can make people crazy, and depending upon the severity, it can make them willing to do almost anything to relieve it! In many cases, surgery is no longer an option due to age or poor overall health. Sometimes, a surgery's outcome is good, but sometimes there is greater pain after the surgery. It can be risky the older one gets. Somehow, we all think that surgery will guarantee a pain-free outcome, but that is not always the case. With pain, there needs to be pain control, and there are many choices to manage and help control it. Below are just a few suggestions to help control your parents' pain:

- Prayer
- Medication
- Herbs
- Acupuncture
- Yoga
- Meditation
- The Green Cure

With the list above and possibly some of your own ideas for pain control, begin to help your parent figure out the right solutions for themselves. Don't take away their right to choose, but help guide and navigate them in making some healthy new decisions. Always keep in mind their state of mind and that no parent, at any age, wants to be controlled by their child. Once again, remember: *respect, honor, and dignity.*

HELPFUL TIP 8

Don't wait to fill out important documents. There are matters at stake that need to be addressed as soon as possible, the earlier the better. Include your parent in this process if they are able so you can be sure to follow their wishes and requests on their directives.

CHAPTER 9

PERSONAL DOCUMENTS

"A place for everything, everything in its place."

— Benjamin Franklin

In the last chapter, we discussed legal documents and the rights of your parent. In this chapter, we will cover personal information, including, but not limited to, passwords, bank accounts, safety deposit boxes, funeral arrangements, life insurance policies, and other important information. You will need to have this information on record before your loved one's memory is stolen by dementia, long-term illness, or just simple aging. Often, once your parent is gone, so is the vital information. There are still ways to find the information you need, but keep in mind that it will take more time and effort than if you had started asking questions sooner.

Earlier in this book, I told how my father thrust me into the instruction of legal and personal documents and what role those documents play in a person's life. I am now grateful that I learned this information so it can benefit so many others, including you. At first, the information can be overwhelming, so I hope this chapter will help you through all the piles of papers.

I would suggest that along with having *The Personal Health Care Manual* for your parent, you purchase a large, red three-ring binder to hold all their financial information, including the papers we discuss in this chapter. This will serve to remind you to be very cautious with the information inside and to keep it in a safe place at home. In the event *The Personal Health Care Manual* is accidentally left at the doctor's office or the hospital, your parent's financial/personal information will not be in jeopardy.

Below, I have created several categories for you to consider when recording your parent's personal information. Take the time to record the information and find a safe place to keep it secured. Again, do not put this information in your parent's *The Personal Health Care Manual.* I have found that as I instruct and guide families, this portion of the discussion has been one of the most helpful in organizing their parent's personal affairs. Asking these questions may feel intrusive, but remember to request the information with the *respect, honor, and dignity* they deserve for being so candid with you.

Let me advise you to take this section slowly and not rush through it in one sitting. It will be exhausting for you and your parent, so be sensitive to their voice, mood, and body language. They will let you know when they have done enough for that day, so your job is to acknowledge it and stop. Let's begin with banks and safety deposit boxes.

BANKS

Name of bank and location:

____

Type of account:

____

Account number:

____

Account name:

____

Signers on account:

____

Password:

____

Name of bank and location:

____

Type of account:

____

Account number:

____

Account name:

____

Signers on account:

____

Password:

____

Name of bank and location:

____

Type of account:

____

Account number:

____

Account name:

____

Signers on account:

____

Password:

____

SAFETY DEPOSIT BOX

Name of bank and location:

___

Where is the key?

___

Box number:

___

Signers on the box:

___

What is inside?

___

ASSETS

Where are the statements and records?

___

Name of broker and location:

___

Type of account or investment:

___

Account number:

____

Account name:

____

Signers on account:

____

Password:

____

PASSWORDS

Computer: ______________________________________

Email address: __________________________________

Email password: _________________________________

Apple ID: ______________________________________

Facebook: ______________________________________

Medical: _______________________________________

Internet access: _________________________________

LinkedIn: ______________________________________

Safe and location: ____________________

Other: ____________________

IMPORTANT KEYS

Key to the house: ____________________

Car keys: ____________________

Post Office Box key: ____________________

Location of the PO Box: ____________________

Post Office Box number: ____________________

ADDITIONAL KEYS

Vacation home: ____________________

Rental Property: ____________________

Miscellaneous keys: ____________________

PRECIOUS METALS AND COINS

Location of the items and where to sell if needed:

____

____

____

PERSONAL COLLECTIONS

Art, jewelry, records, stones, figurines, cars, etc.

____

____

HIDDEN TREASURE

Where it is located and what it looks like:

____

____

LIFE INSURANCE POLICY

Name of the policy holder:

____

Where is the policy kept?

____

Name of company:

____

Mailing address:

____

Contact information:

____

Phone:

____

Email:

____

LONG-TERM CARE INSURANCE

Name of the policy holder:

____

Where is the policy kept?

____

Name of insurance company:

____

Mailing address:

____

Contact information:

____

Phone:

____

Email:

____

VETERAN (VA) BENEFITS

Yes, I qualify for benefits.

My Honorable Discharge papers (DD-214) are located:

____

____

I wish to be buried at a Military cemetery: ________________

Where: ____________________________________

____

Contact: Veteran's Administration website at www.va.gov

MORTGAGE PAPERS, TITLES, AND DEEDS

Where are they located?

____

____

WILLS AND TESTAMENTS

Where are they located?

____

____

THINGS TO GIVE AWAY TO SPECIAL PEOPLE OR ORGANIZATIONS

____

____

____

____

____

____

____

HELPFUL TIP 9

The importance of securing and organizing important forms and resources is paramount in your ability to be present for your parent when they need you most.

CHAPTER 10

INVOLVING FAMILY AND FRIENDS

"Unity is strength...when there is teamwork and collaboration, wonderful things can be achieved."

— Mattie Stefanik

MR. JOHNSTON'S STORY

A year and a half ago, I was working with a client named Bruce. One day, he informed me that his father, Mr. Johnston had been, once again, in the hospital and had been sent to an SNF (skilled nursing facility) for rehabilitation. The assessment was that Mr. Johnston no longer needed the care of the nursing facility and would be released early the following week. That was the good news. The bad news was he would no longer be able to live independently at home without support. The major concern was his safety and who would provide his supervision. It is common practice for a skilled nursing facility to arrange a care conference for the patient and their family prior to a release from the facility. All the key members in Mr. Johnston's care were included in this conference, including the OT (occupational therapist), PT (physical therapist), head of the nursing department, social worker, and so on. Each came to inform the family of Mr. Johnston's progress and give recommendations.

It was suggested that Mr. Johnston needed extra help at home or he would need to be moved to an ALF (assisted living facility).

Mr. Johnston had been a physicist in his day, and he was married with five children. He had spent much time deep in thought, but he had also managed to do well for himself and be a good provider for his family. His children all grew up, became professionals themselves, and began families of their own. At age seventy-six, Mrs. Johnston passed away, leaving Mr. Johnston all alone in the big family home in Portland.

At age eighty-five, Mr. Johnston's health began to suffer and life began to include more visits to the doctor and the emergency room. Eventually, more hospitalizations became necessary. As Mr. Johnston became physically weaker with each visit, his family began to take notice. His children, now in their late fifties and early sixties, were still holding down jobs and leading busy lives. Four of the five children lived within the same state and within an hour's drive or less. Only one of his children lived out of state.

With the concerns presented, the family was faced with the looming question: "What do we do with Dad?" During a patient care conference at the nursing facility, I watched in dismay as the family began to *try* to discuss the matter, which rather quickly turned into a heated argument with raised voices. Fingers were pointed and rude accusations flew. I directed my eyes to Mr. Johnston, who was seated in a wheelchair between two of his daughters as if he were invisible. His head was drooped to his chest and his shoulders were rounded in as if to say: "STOP...just stop now!" to his snarling children.

"A man of few words," was how I would have previously described Mr. Johnston's character, and that day was no different. Some people can remain silent during the worst rudeness or insensitivity, but I sensed that day that Mr. Johnston was an introvert. Had his family ever understood him, or was their current behavior how they always interacted? Either way, I witnessed their disharmony as a family, which presented itself as hurt and blame thrown back and forth like fiery, flaming arrows. Was this reaction actually about Mr. Johnston's current wavering health, or was it about a group of siblings, young daughters and sons, with unmet needs who had spent a lifetime with a man who rarely spoke to them? Were they just unwilling to be helpful because of past hurts and a lack of forgiveness? Whatever the root cause, it was turning into a caustic situation.

One of the daughters decided Mr. Johnston should be moved to a nursing home for long-term care. She felt his needs would be fully met there. Bruce, her brother, who was also Mr. Johnston's Power of Attorney, objected because his father wasn't in poor enough health to warrant such care. Bruce was passionate that his father would not end up just sitting in a wheelchair with a distant dazestruck look on his face, trapped somewhere in Never Neverland.

As the discussion intensified, I finally rose to my feet and interrupted the mayhem by asking one simple question: "Has anyone asked *your father* what his wishes are?" Everyone fell silent and all eyes turned toward their father. It seemed they had all forgotten he was sitting among them around the big brown table. Bruce quietly rose from his chair and leaned across the table toward his father. With a calm and gentle voice, he asked, "Dad, where would *you* like to go?" His father slowly raised his weary head from his chest, looked at Bruce, and said, "I want to go home, son."

You could have heard a pin drop. I again rose to my feet and explained that there were still other alternatives to a nursing home. I strongly encouraged Bruce and his siblings to arrange a follow-up family meeting at another time due to the situation getting so out of hand. The family still had time to make final decisions about their father and could continue the discussion when their tempers were less sour.

What I had surmised from the meeting was that Bruce wanted his siblings to step up, take responsibility, and share some of their father's overall care. The reality was that the majority of them were not interested in helping.

As I counseled Bruce later that afternoon, my words were swift and to the point: "We *cannot* make anyone do anything they do not want to do. They have to want to do it or it will never happen. The only person you can change is you and how you look at the situation." Bruce was stunned because his siblings really didn't want to help.

Because no man (or woman) is an island, it can be very stressful and exhausting to care for an aging or ill parent; you may find this is the time to begin looking for help outside the family and inside the community.

Surprisingly, you may find your parent's friends or church family are more than happy to show support for your parent. A mowed lawn, a yummy home-cooked meal, freshly baked cookies, or just some quality time with your parent are examples of some of the ways unexpected support can show up.

On occasion, I do come across families (and friends) who are willing to operate as a team and participate in the care of Mom and Dad. How wonderful that is, and what a blessing in turn for their parent. In these scenarios, everyone is willing to help out in whatever big or small way possible to lessen the load for the whole. Families today live all over the globe, so sometimes the distance is just too great for a daily visit, let alone helping out physically. With that in mind, family members need to know there are still many other ways to help and show support. The biggest key is for everyone to continue having a healthy attitude toward the situation and one another.

Sometimes, involving family and friends in the care of your parent can be very difficult; it's a sensitive issue. Many family members may be very eager and willing to get involved, but you may also find some members of your family don't want any part in it, even to the smallest degree.

This is where extra grace comes in to help with coping, to work through challenging relationships, and the awareness of early grief. As you may recall, in Chapter 1, we discussed your relationship with your parent, and your parent's relationships with others. Many times, people are apprehensive to participate due to sadness, denial, grief, or even anger. These are all part of the grief cycle that will affect your coping skills when it comes to loss. Grief takes many forms. For some people in this situation, recognizing a parent's loss of independence and the need to assist them can be troubling.

You wake up one day and that big strong dad you once had now uses a walker and cane, or maybe your mom, who had always been a good listener and offered her time and energy so freely, is showing signs of memory loss and confusion, and this realization just rocks your world.

All of this may cause you to step back and reflect on what both you and they were like in younger days. Time has moved on, and so should you and your siblings. This may sound and feel harsh, but it is the truth. I encourage you and the support team to read Chapter 17: Processing Grief. It will help you understand each other better emotionally, and it will aid you in conflicts that may occur. Remember, your parent is also walking through their own grief and loss. Don't miss Chapter 12 where I talk about how to look outside your family for further resources and support.

While you may request help from a specific family member repeatedly, that person still might not want to help and will come up with every excuse in the book why he or she is unavailable to spare even the smallest amount of time. At times, you will wonder why you still bother to ask for help because certain family members don't seem to be available to give you *any* relief, or even just a few moments of their time so you can rest, attend your son's school concert, a doctor's appointment, or a date night with your spouse. You may become frustrated, angry, and resentful and think to yourself: "What is the problem? For goodness sake, she's your mom too!"

For a long time, I thought this reluctance to help was only found in my family, but as time went on and I started to help other families, I found out many families taking care of a parent have similar circumstances with unhelpful family members. Whether it's a family of two children or six, one sibling usually becomes the primary caregiver of the parent and is responsible for everything from the actual caregiving all the way down to being the Power of Attorney.

VULNERABILITY

Webster defines vulnerable as: susceptible to physical harm, damage, or emotional injury.

In my opinion, the person *most* vulnerable here is the primary caregiver in the family.

The term "caregiver" applies not only to the hired help, but also to the family member most responsible for another's care and welfare, such as a parent. The term may also pertain to a spouse, sibling, neighbor, or friend. Whether the care is given daily or as needed, a caregiver is the one responsible for someone else's care.

In most cases, I have found it to be the spouse or an adult child who becomes the primary caregiver because he or she is usually providing the care on a daily basis. This role may or may not include assisting in the physical care of a loved one; for some, this task is hired out. The primary caregiver, in this case, is still the one handling all the other affairs pertinent to the individual's care, and is also the one who needs the most support and encouragement on a regular basis. Statistics say that 60 percent of caregivers end up on the floor before their loved one does. What does that mean? It means caregivers tend to wear themselves out and overlook their own personal needs. You must learn to manage your own needs so you can stay healthy enough to care for your loved one/parent. Putting *some* of your personal needs first is necessary, but not always easy; you'll have to work at it, but you'll thank me in the morning.

Back in Chapter 3, we covered some items to help you take care of yourself as you practice being a caregiver. Here are some other helpful tips from Rosalynn Carter's book *Helping Yourself Help Others*:

1. Listen to your friends; be open to others' observations.
2. Let go; know your limits.
3. Focus on your loved one's strengths.
4. Learn relaxation techniques.
5. Take care of your health.
6. Maintain a life outside of your caregiving role.
7. Take advantage of some down time.
8. Build a caregiving team.
9. Rely on your sense of humor.
10. Appreciate the benefits of leisure time.
11. Help your loved one find a support group.
12. Seek professional help.
13. Appreciate your own efforts.
14. Seek spiritual renewal.

You will also need to learn to ask for help (more about this in

Chapter 11). Don't be reluctant to ask the neighbor to pick up your mail the same time he gets his and drop it by, or your son to mow the lawn, or your children to help with cleaning or cooking a few meals. Life is busy no matter where you're standing, but *learn* to let your support in.

FOLLOWING THE LEADER

In most families, a leader usually springs up during troubling times. Leadership and advocacy go hand in hand. In Chapter 6, we discussed advocacy at length. If you haven't read Chapter 6, this might be a good time to go back and read it. If *you* are the leader, you will also find yourself in the position of having to advocate frequently for your parent.

The leader may turn out to be the oldest in the family, but don't be surprised if it's the youngest. Do yourself a favor and don't get caught up in the drama and judgment of "Why didn't so-and-so step up to help out?" Just be thankful someone is willing to step up to the plate. This is a good example of another time when you can practice and apply the *respect, honor, and dignity* concept. Help your family members and friends understand this concept too, and know there will be stressful and uncertain times when it seems the whole family system is falling apart. It will be up to you to bring the focus back when stability goes out the window because you have a knowledge base after reading this book that others may not have. If everyone on board begins to practice *respect, honor, and dignity*, the entire journey will become easier.

PARTICIPATION

You may find that your family and friends have a different frame of reference and perspective because they have experienced their relationships with your parent differently. This is important to remember because the past plays a huge part in the future. Anticipate that each person will have his or her own personal experience and feelings in response to the illness of the loved one, and that's *okay—really*.

Everyone's coping skills may be different, and people express their feelings, including grief and loss, in their own ways (more about this in Chapter 17). Some people may appear stoic or very emotional at times and go from one extreme to the other. We need to give one another grace and allow others to be who they are; accept them and move forward. Again, do your best to stay out of judgment.

As the team develops and each member assumes his or her position, everyone will begin to learn and practice new roles and things will begin to work. Don't get your knickers in a bunch over the small stuff because the stakes are high and it will be important to continue working together as a team. One great way to keep the team in alignment and to support each other is by holding "family meetings."

PREPARING FOR A FAMILY MEETING

To prepare for your family meeting, you will need to define what type of meeting you want to have. Some considerations should include:

- Are you going to conduct the meeting yourself or do you need an advocate?

- Will it be an informal meeting, a working and planning meeting, or a decision-making meeting?
- What is the meeting's purpose and goal, and what is the desired outcome?
- What approach should you take, and how best will you be heard by your siblings or other family members?
- Is it possible you are still being viewed by your family members in the same role you once had growing up?
- Is your family concerned about your past track record and now doesn't understand why *you* want to take the helm?

Thinking of potential considerations in advance can help you gain clarity should these important topics come up.

HOLDING FAMILY MEETINGS

The simple who, what, where, when, and how method can be used at your meeting. Don't forget to have someone take notes. For example:

1. What needs to be done currently?

____

____

____

____

____

2. Who is responsible to complete the tasks?

____

____

____

____

____

3. Where and when do the tasks need to be accomplished?

____

____

____

____

____

4. How will the tasks be accomplished?

____

____

____

____

____

Because time is precious to everyone, you will need a commitment from each family member (or friend) to participate in the family meetings so everyone is receiving the same information and is clear on his or her tasks and timeline. If someone absolutely can't be in attendance at the meeting, can he or she be available by phone or Skype to listen to the meeting? If not, designate someone who is present at the meeting to fill in the absent person on the details later so nothing slips through the cracks. Today, there are so many ways to communicate. This may be a good time to increase your own skill set and learn some new ways technology can help you stay in the loop.

A few years ago, I had been asked to conduct a family meeting for one of my clients. All of the adult children were gathered together in the living room of one of their homes. In the middle of the coffee table was a computer that was opened with another brother and his wife sitting on their sofa, engaged in the conversation from their living room in Oklahoma, ready and poised for the meeting. It was great to have them take part in the family meeting and get their input in real time.

Telephone calls, emails, and texting are all great, but face-to-face meetings or Skype are more personal, and information is much less likely to get lost in translation when everyone is in the same room together.

I would suggest having an initial meeting to start with, and then, when a "plan" is developed and people begin taking on supportive roles, ongoing meetings can be scheduled as needed. At times, new situations will arise and you'll find you are spending too much time on the phone or texting at length about the new information so a better use of your time would be to call another meeting to get everyone on the same page again. It is much easier and more time-effective to tell the story once rather than four times.

Be sure to establish the concept of *respect, honor, and dignity* at the very first meeting, and make it the focus for all the team members to pivot around in every conversation and with everyone they interact with. Again, *respect, honor, and dignity* is the foundation of healthy relationships. If you have been blessed with a great family system that works well, good communication should already be in place.

Having family and friends willing to do their part is all you really need. It's not that each member needs to be an expert in any given field of training to know everything; each one just needs to be willing to lend a hand and be part of the journey. Many hands make work light, and being willing and available are the only keys, even if your time is limited. Be kind and courteous to one another, and if you can work as a team, that, for sure, will be the best way to go.

You've heard it said, "It takes a village to raise a child." Well, I believe it takes a team to care for an aging parent. Each situation is different, but the underlying need for compassion and understanding is always the same. Addressing your parents' needs and discussing the specifics as a family/team will determine the most prevalent areas that need attention. Be sure to meet with your parent to *listen* to and help them identify their personal needs as they make requests about their own care. Share your findings with your family team at a different time and location. I have provided some great questions for discussion, which can help your family team define the roles of each member.

DISCUSSION

1. Who will provide the bathing and hygiene (and when)?
2. Who will be able to attend medical appointments?
3. Who will pick up pharmacy items, groceries, mail, etc.?
4. Who will be doing the meal preparation and cooking?
5. Who will do the cleaning and housekeeping?
6. Who will do the laundry and change the bedding?
7. Will someone else need to provide transportation?
8. Who will come during the weekdays to check in?
9. Who is available in the evenings?
10. Who is available on the weekend?
11. Who should be called/emailed first in case of an emergency?

Finding out what each person feels comfortable and confident doing will make the designation and completion of tasks easier for everyone. *Not everyone* is comfortable doing certain tasks, so give team members a chance to volunteer first rather than assigning tasks and see how it goes. This process can mean the difference between frustration and wholehearted giving.

For the more challenging tasks, work together as a team to find the solution that works best. This may include hiring help from outside the family, which is not a bad thing.

If tensions arise, remember what I said before about learning how to give grace to one another and move on. Say you're sorry, forgive, and begin again on the journey you *all* are on. *Remember, at this point, it's not about you.* I say that with a genuine heart. There comes a time when the focus should be solely on your parent's needs and not yours, even though some of your own needs are unmet. Recognize these times and know that the tough times will pass; they are only for a season.

HELPFUL TIP 10

Allow yourself to be pliable as you work together to establish the best care for your parent. This is the time to answer important questions that will help you best assist your parent.

CHAPTER 11
LIFE INTERRUPTED

"The truth is, of course, that what one regards as interruptions are precisely one's life."

— C.S. Lewis

DODGING BULLETS

Late last fall, I met with a woman named Helga who was contemplating heart surgery. She told me her cardiologist had informed her one of her heart valves wasn't closing correctly so surgery was necessary. At age eighty-three, this would be Helga's very first surgery should she decide to go through with it, and she was struggling to make the decision. She had asked the doctor numerous questions and spoken with many friends; yes, Helga had done her homework.

Helga was also informed that without the surgery to replace her heart valve, her body would soon begin to experience increased fatigue and limited abilities. In other words, her life was hanging in the balance. The first thing we discussed was whether she would have family support or any other support should she choose to have the surgery.

She shared with me that as a young girl, in 1940, she had escaped East Germany to flee to freedom while running through bullet fire. Her story was one of extreme bravery. Once she was able to escape, she sailed across the Atlantic Ocean to begin a new life in Canada as a young, single woman. She really was all alone since she came without any family.

Helga married later in life to a wonderful man who adored her, and she adored him. It was a fulfilling marriage, and they were so in love. They had a lovely home in Seattle that her husband had taken great care of, doing much of the work with his own loving hands. Helga was so proud of his handiwork.

Helga and her husband were both hard workers, but mostly, they just loved to be around one another. I so enjoyed watching Helga's face as she shared about her husband. Her eyes would smile and dance as she spoke, and a beautiful, warm, and gentle smile would tiptoe across her lips. Her smile was reminiscent of young love. "I really miss him," she would say, and her smile would fade away as if it were all a dream. Helga's husband, Henry, had passed away thirteen years prior, once again leaving her on her own.

Helga had always been physically and emotionally strong, but now she was facing something new. She had no children or family to lean on, much less step in to help care for her. Change was afoot, and Helga's life was about to be interrupted in a big way. But where do you go for help and support when there is no family nearby, or even more daunting, when there is no family available or living? This is not an unusual circumstance. In this chapter, we will discuss resources and help for both those who already have the support of family and those who may not.

DRASTICALLY ALTERED

Let me share here another story of having one's life interrupted. It concerns some friends my husband and I met during a cruise. We met Tom and Beverly across the dining room table. Tom was a policeman and Beverly had been a preschool teacher. Their devotion and love for one another shined like the bright sun, but an event from three years earlier was still rearranging their future. Although they were still not really sure where life was heading, they were committed to laughter, love, and pressing forward with full knowledge that a difficult journey lay ahead of them.

Tom, a man with hope and dance in his eyes and face as he spoke, had a gentle smile to complement his sun-tanned complexion. Beverly, a woman with life in her gentle and meaningful touch, had a delightful squeal of joy that prompted you to join in her enthusiasm over something that had just brought delight to her spirit.

That evening, Beverly and I exchanged the usual girl talk about our jewelry and fingernail polish. We talked about our children and Tom and Beverly's grandchildren, some married with kids, and some single with cats. We shared our adventures and follies of the day in Jamaica over a lamb dinner, dessert, and coffee.

The conversation was delightful, and somehow, I felt as if God had put us there, at that table, at that precious moment in time. I believe God loves me, so I know He also leads me. Did I go searching this time, or had He just done His usual? You know what I mean… the unexpected, in the middle of the big, blue ocean? Yes, somewhere between the Yucatan and Cuba on a cruise ship, the Lord was still at work!

What I didn't tell you was that Beverly was in a wheelchair. Her life had been drastically altered three years before by a routine knee surgery. As her husband Tom unfolded their story, bit by bit, the compassion in my heart grew roots for them. Their story seemed to me like buying tickets to a dream vacation in France and instead ending up in Siberia with no way back home.

Beverly had suffered a severe stroke in the operating room three years earlier during her knee surgery. After her surgery, she was not the same woman. Her life had been permanently changed, and so had her husband's. Her motor skills were affected so she could no longer walk or care for herself independently. From then on, she would need a wheelchair and help in all areas, including feeding. She had difficulty speaking and needed her husband's constant help, sometimes just to translate her words. I leaned in close most of the time as we chatted so I could follow her the best I could without her husband's help because I wanted to honor her with my listening. For the most part, I could follow her conversation, but with the noise of other conversations circling about in the dining room, I would periodically have to lean on Tom's voice for aid.

I found it a delight to share the dinner table with them that night. I wouldn't have missed it! I learned so much from both of them that evening about coping with the unexpected. What does the future hold for them? I have no idea, and neither do they. Were they prepared for this? No way, but it happened. This is why preparation is so important and necessary.

Another great story and example of having to change (being forced really into change) is that of my eighty-four-year-old father-in-law whom I dearly loved. His illness was a major interruption in *his* life and ours, but it was also a major turning point and a huge lesson in coping with change.

It had been seven years since my mother-in-law passed away, and now my father-in-law had become our concern. From level nine chest pain, prostrate cancer, and stage three renal failure to uncontrolled diabetes and a potential foot amputation, Dad desperately tried to continue to survive. He had his daily bridge games to attend, the stock market to track, and his stamp collection to sort and file.

There were days when it took all he could muster just to get out of bed to travel to one of his bridge games somewhere in the city. He lived for the game. He played five to six days a week and loved it. He also loved the cookies and tea that came with it. But now he was failing much faster than ever before. His needs had become greater, and he wasn't bouncing back as fast.

At this point, Dad was still thinking he could walk, and on rare occasions he could, but he needed plenty of assistance and his walker. He would take a few steps and his legs would give way. He was very determined to keep trying to walk on his own, but it wasn't a good choice to allow him to do it. He was becoming so much weaker that it had become too dangerous even to let him try. His life was lived in only two places—his recliner or his bed—and he spent 95 percent of the time in either place, asleep. Even food and eating no longer seemed to hold enjoyment and pleasure for him; they had become more of a chore and annoyance.

Along with having to accept and process the changes that occur in our parent's life (and our own) as we age or deal with illness, we have to learn how to ask for help. This vulnerability can be difficult for people who are used to being self-sufficient, or who are used to their parents being strong, healthy, and independent. The next story describes a woman's turning point as she learns to begin asking for help.

ASKING FOR HELP

One Thursday afternoon in late July, I received a phone call from a woman named Ruth who had been referred to me by a mutual friend. Ruth was a warm and delightful seventy-eight-year-old woman who was still living in her own home of fifty years. She had been a widow for the past eight years, had no children, and her only living relatives resided in Greece, thousands of miles away. To her advantage, Ruth did have family of the heart that she had adopted many years earlier, and they likewise had adopted her. She also had several neighbors who provided a caring, watchful eye over her and assisted her when possible. We scheduled a meeting, at her home, for the end of the week, and there her story unfolded.

On April 3, Ruth was alone in her home and found herself suffering from severe shaking, dizziness, and vomiting. She called a neighbor for help, and with her assistance and the emergency room nurse on the telephone, the emergency response team got her to safety at the local hospital. She was diagnosed with heart trouble.

Ruth remained at the hospital for several days to recover before being released to go home. She received some care at home through her medical plan. The policy also included more assistance to her, if and when the need should arise. This care included physical and occupational therapy, a visiting nurse, and a shower aide. This was all covered under her medical benefits, so there was no added expense to her pocketbook.

Six weeks after that medical incident, Ruth returned to the emergency room with the same issue. Six hours later, she was released and referred to her regular doctor for a follow up. Weeks later, and on proper medication for her heart, she began to think about what she would do if she were hospitalized and then needed to be admitted to a nursing home for rehabilitation. For Ruth, the most concerning question was: Where will I go, and do I have a choice in the location?

We spoke at length about the situation. I asked many questions and listened intensely as she shared her likes, dislikes, and some of her fears. We have all seen those nursing homes/rehabilitation centers that we would never dream of sending our worst enemy to, let alone our parent. We all fear those types of places, and so did she.

Here are some of the questions I asked Ruth to begin our plan of action:

1. What type of medical coverage do you have?
2. Do you have any additional medical coverage?
3. Are you on Medicare?
4. Are there any restrictions in your health plan that limit which skilled nursing facilities (SNF) you can rehabilitate at?
5. Are you aware of the amount of days you can stay in a nursing facility for rehabilitation before you have to begin paying out of pocket?
6. Have you visited any friends in nursing homes in your area, and would you be willing to go to any of those homes? Why?
7. Are there other facilities you would be willing to go to if you needed to?
8. Who or what would you like to be closest to if you needed to go into a facility for rehabilitation?
9. What matters most: the cost, the food, the care, or the atmosphere of the place?
10. Are there any places you would *not* want to stay at?

Use the space below to answer these questions for *your* parent.

1. ______________________________

2. ______________________________

3. ______________________________

4. ______________________________

5. ______________________________

6. ______________________________

7. ______________________________

8. ______________________________

9. ______________________________

10. ______________________________

As Ruth and I concluded this topic and made plans to meet again the following week to complete her *Personal Health Care Manual*, I then approached a new topic I knew she really needed to give some important thought to. I wanted her to begin thinking down the road a bit because, despite her illness, she might live another ten years or more.

Ruth had always been a self-reliant woman, so she had many of her legal and financial ducks in a row, but another topic needed further decision: What would happen if she were no longer able to stay in her home? She had been there for more than fifty years! What would be her second choice, and would her second choice be something she might consider taking advantage of now before it got to the point of being forced upon her when she was no longer able to make the decision on her own?

It is never too early to have this discussion with your loved one, but it can be too late, and then the choice could potentially be out of their hands. Aging is inevitable, and when illness is added to the mix, there will be major interruptions in your life and theirs. How will you cope with the change and the interruption? How are you currently coping? Let me remind you that you will gain great tools and tips on handling interruptions and change by reading all the chapters in this book. To gain the most out of this book, be sure to answer the questions and fill in the blanks; your answers will serve as your personal roadmap for what to do next.

HELPFUL TIP 11

It is important for your parent to consider their options as early as possible on this journey. Consider approaching your loved one with important questions sooner than later to give them autonomy and an active voice in their own care. Err on the side of quickness because you never know when it may be too late.

CHAPTER 12

FINDING RESOURCES

"We have to tell people who need help that it's OK to ask for it."

— Macklemore

First and foremost, you will need to recognize and identify your parent's needs. Some of their needs might be immediate while new and different needs may surface in the upcoming months or possibly year ahead. At the same time, it will be equally as important to recognize your own needs. *Don't keep your head in the sand because time can move quickly when illness begins.*

Use the space below to list your parent's needs, and place a checkmark next to the items that are immediate. (Use a separate sheet if needed.)

1. ____

2. ______________________________

3. ______________________________

4. ______________________________

5. ______________________________

6. ______________________________

7. ______________________________

8. ______________________________

9. ______________________________

10. ______________________________

Be honest with yourself because your needs are just as important as your parents and you will need to remain healthy throughout this journey. Now, think of *your* needs and list them below:

1. ______________________________

2. ______________________________

3. ______________________________

4. ______________________________

5. ______________________________

6. ______________________________

7. ______________________________

8. ______________________________

9. ______________________________

10. ______________________________

Both your parent's and *your* needs are important, and it really helps to be clear on what those needs are so you can be vigilant in making sure they are being met to the best of your ability.

A helpful suggestion is to rest when your parent rests or you may end up becoming exhausted. Be sure to get enough sleep because each day (and night) has its own challenges.

I understand that free time may be hard to come by if you are the primary caregiver and your parent requires much of your time and attention, but trying to push through your own exhaustion is not a good idea. Learn to rest a bit—yes, "a bit"—when your parent rests. You will regain some strength and energy for when they wake up and need you again, rather than using what little spare time you have to tackle a major project or two.

Respite—I just love that word. It reminds me to "rest for a bit." The word actually means a short rest or relief from something difficult or unpleasant. Synonyms for respite include reprieve, postponement, deferment, delay, and just plain old rest. In essence, what I am suggesting is to learn to take a respite for yourself whenever you can.

When your parent's health begins to deteriorate, your parent will have an even greater need for care. They will need more emotional care and more physical help, which takes a greater toll on the caregiver.

A broader concept of respite is specifically related to this more intensive level of care. If your parent remains in their own home or yours, and the caregiver is a family member, be sure to look into "respite care" for your parent. This care is often covered under health insurance, so make sure to refer to your parent's policy; it may require a phone call or two to check on their benefits. If they qualify for Medicare or Medicaid benefits, find out what those agencies can do to help.

As a reminder, if you are unfamiliar with some of the vocabulary I use throughout the book, please refer to the Learning New Terminology section in Chapter 6.

PROGRAMS AND BENEFITS

Here are some of the first questions to think about when you are looking for resources to help your parent:

1. Where do I look?
2. What's the cost?
3. Will my parent accept the help?

My mother lived in an apartment building operated by the county where she resided. It was a nice and clean three-story apartment building, and its residents always kept a good eye on one another. A few tenants made it a practice to check in on those who were under the weather or to lend a hand if someone were having some difficulty. They always covered for each other whenever they could. They had created a community among themselves.

Other residents kept to themselves, and on occasion, there were a couple of feisty ones, but all in all, it was a good place for my mother to live. Some residents had chore workers who came to help with their daily chores such as cleaning, shopping, and laundry. Some had caregivers to aid in bathing and wound care. I took note about what was happening in the building and began to ask some questions. *Frequently, programs and benefits are out there that people are privy to, but the average individual may be unaware of what may be available.* Start asking!

After asking many questions, I learned my mom qualified for numerous benefits due to her low-income status. I was aware of some of these benefits before my mother moved into the community, but plenty more were still up for the taking. Of course, there was always plenty of paperwork involved, but it was well worth the effort. If I had left this task up to my mom to complete, it would have *never happened*! Not that my mother was lazy, but there were pages and pages of repetitive required information. Then, there were weeks of "the waiting game" before you knew whether you had received approval.

Below are some of the benefits your parent may qualify for if they have little in assets. Place a checkmark beside the ones you think may apply:

- ☐ Low-Income Housing
- ☐ Reduced Telephone Rate
- ☐ EBT Card (for food)
- ☐ Heating Assistance

- ☐ Food Bank Privileges
- ☐ Clothing Bank Privileges
- ☐ Chore Workers
- ☐ Medicaid
- ☐ Reduced Cost Dental Care
- ☐ Transportation Assistance

These are just a few areas of assistance that may be available through the many different agencies in your community, including your state government's Department of Social and Health Services. *Numerous programs are available, so it is well worth your time and effort to do the research.* Just to get you started, check www.benefitscheckup.gov for eligibility and find local services at www.eldercarelocator.gov.

How do you find out whether your parent qualifies for any assistance or program? Begin by contacting the Department of Social and Health Services (DSHS). You can do this on the internet or find the number in your local phone book. The Department of Social and Health Services is run by both the Federal and local government. It offers programs nationwide.

Keep in mind that each state and county offer different programs, so investigate and gather the information pertinent to your parent. While this process may take considerable time, potentially months, remember to be courteous and patient, even though the process can be frustrating.

CONTACTING AGENCIES

Each county and state in the United States provides different resources to the public. Your job is to find what is available in your parent's location. To give you an idea of some of the many resources out there, I have provided a list of Community Resources available in two of the major counties in Washington State, where I reside:

- ☐ Senior Information and Assistance-statewide
- ☐ SHIBA: Statewide Health Insurance Benefits Advisor
- ☐ Meals on Wheels and Mobile Market-Senior Services
- ☐ Respite Care Program
- ☐ Adult Day Health Programs
- ☐ Volunteer Chore Program
- ☐ Department of Social and Health Services, Home and Community Services (COPES)
- ☐ Community Services for the Blind and Partially Low Vision Clinic
- ☐ Hearing, Speech & Deaf Center
- ☐ Minor Home Repair
- ☐ Transportation-Volunteer Rides

As previously mentioned, the names of these organizations may vary from state to state.

WHEN TO HIRE OUTSIDE HELP

Here are some important indicators to consider when you begin wondering whether it may be time to get some outside help:

- ☐ When the needs of your parent are greater than you can manage
- ☐ When your own health is diminishing
- ☐ When your body is telling you so
- ☐ When you don't get 6-8 hours of uninterrupted sleep per night
- ☐ When you no longer can leave your loved one in the house alone more than two hours per day
- ☐ When your friends and family say it's time

If any of these indicators are true for you or the primary caregiver, it is absolutely time to hire outside help. There are many ways to find a great caregiver when the time comes, such as asking around your social circle to see whether your friends might have any referrals, do a Google search on the internet to see what comes up in your area, and check local newspapers and community senior centers for information and to find a reputable agency. Any reputable agency should have stringent screening and background-check processes and professional references, but it is *your* responsibility to do your own screening to ensure the safety of your parent and their home.

Finding a good caregiver and/or agency involves time and energy, so I suggest not waiting until you are burnt out to begin your search.

Taking action is the key.

ADULT FAMILY HOMES

Adult family homes (AFH) are a wonderful option to consider long-term for a parent, and on occasion, these types of homes are used for temporary housing for rehabilitation. Here in the greater

Seattle area, there are many AFHs to choose from. They come in many styles and price ranges. In other parts of the United States, there can be fewer AFHs available, and in some of the smaller cities and towns, there are hardly any. Do some research to find what is available in your parent's area. Contact the State Office on Aging and Disability to see what information it may have to help you. If you are planning to move your parent closer to you, begin your search as soon as you can; planning ahead is so important at this point. Do not forget to ask about the entrance fees and additional charges.

You are probably thinking: *But what exactly is an adult family home?* An AFH looks just like a typical family home from the outside, and some are more elaborate than others. The interior of each home can vary greatly as well. Some will have hardwood floors while others might have vinyl flooring. In Washington State, all AFHs are state regulated and are limited to five or six residents per home. Bedrooms can be single or shared and may have their own off-suite bathroom or a shared bathroom down the hall.

Many AFHs have one common living room, and some homes even include an extra common living area with a library or sitting room with puzzles and quiet activities. Some AFHs even provide residents with weekly/monthly entertainment such as a musicians, vocalists, choral groups, or speakers. Many include outside activities such as gardening and personal flower boxes. Some even have an activity bus for occasional outings and sightseeing.

Many of the newer AFHs offer organic foods and much healthier meals than some of the older facilities, and they have even improved the quality of the drinking water. I am so thrilled to see all of the wonderful and much-needed improvements happening in this area of care.

As I shared earlier, an AFH is a great option to look into for your loved one or parent because the homes are relatively small and, therefore, the care is limited to five or six residents, unlike at a big nursing home facility, which can have less personalized care due to the larger number of residents, and tends to have a much more "institutional" feel. AFHs provide more time for individualized care and attention.

Earlier in this chapter, I had you list your parent's current needs. If at this point you have not completed that task, I would strongly encourage you to go back to that section and fill in your responses. As you look over the options of *where* to move your mom/dad, remember to check out what each place has to offer your parent and how it will also work for you and your family. Is it a place where other family members would be comfortable visiting or having a meal? Is the location close enough for friends and family to visit? Is it a place your parent will get lost in and become known as "Room #223, Bed #2," or will your parent still be called by their name? Will they be honored, respected, and shown dignity? Will their needs be met with kindness and gentleness?

Through my travels and many visits with people over the years, I have come to a surprising conclusion: Not all elderly people are nice! That's correct; not all elderly people are nice. Does that mean they should not be treated nicely? (You do realize this is a test, right?) Will the placement match your parent's needs and demands, and will it provide the safety they need both in their bed as well as out?

It will take time for both you and your parent to adjust to the new place you have chosen and the *new normal.* Your parent may request or even plead with you to take them back home. You have to remember why you moved them in the first place. Look back at the list you made earlier and what *their* needs were; that should be enough to help you stay firm in your decision and not fold. If you find you made a bad placement, consider moving your parent to another facility, but try not to bring them back home unless you can provide the care you were seeking when you first chose to move them. I strongly suggest you do your homework so you can find a good placement the first time.

What do you look for in an AFH? The following is just a basic checklist of things to consider when searching for the right place for mom/dad. This checklist is designed to help you ask the same questions of each home or facility. I would recommend making several copies of the checklist and taking it with you as you tour perspective placement opportunities. It will help keep you on track. Then review the checklists before making any decisions for your parent.

Checklist for Placement

Facility Name: ______________________________________

1. How does it look?
2. Is it clean?
3. How does it smell?
4. Are the employees friendly and kind?

5. Do the residents look happy and content?
6. Do the residents look clean?
7. What foods do they serve?
8. Is the food fresh and homemade?
9. What are the mealtimes?
10. How many residents live there?
11. What is the ratio between residents and caregivers?
12. What time is wake-up and bedtime?
13. What activities do they provide?
14. Is there any entertainment/stimuli coming into the site on a regular basis?
15. What are the visiting hours?
16. Is there any outdoor space to sit?
17. Who provides the bedroom furniture?
18. Can you bring your favorite chair, recliner, and/or TV?
19. Does the facility accept long-term care insurance or Medicaid?
20. Can my parent stay here until end of life?

Take a few moments to jot down some of your own questions and concerns prior to placing your parent into an AFH or any facility.

LONG-TERM CARE FACILITIES

The term "long-term care" refers to full-time care until end of life. When an individual enters a Nursing Facility or SNF for rehabilitation only from illness, injury, or surgery, that individual will receive around-the-clock care. The stay will usually include some form of therapy to improve and enhance their physical abilities so they can eventually return home. Occupational and physical therapy are usually given to improve movement, coordination, and mobility. After several weeks of care, if the individual has continued to improve, he or she is then released to return back home.

When an individual is no longer able to be cared for at home or is not progressing with rehabilitation, a long-term care living situation then needs to be sought out for the individual.

Long-term care facilities consist of AFHs, SNFs, nursing homes and facilities, and finally, memory care facilities. Learn to listen to those around you who have experienced a good facility as well as a bad one. When the time comes to make the move for your parent, try to be ahead of the game, and have some options already sought out because the need can happen suddenly, so be prepared.

Seek the help of a placement agency if you can because it will have more connections to the community and the staff will be familiar with what is available and in which locations. Let the agency do the hard work of searching for a location, making the phone calls, and setting up appointments around your schedule while you spend time with your parent and family.

Just a quick word of advice: If you find the placement agent you are working with is too pushy or you feel the agent is not providing a quality job, ask for someone else to serve you or find a different company. It happened to me so I learned a great lesson.

Who pays the bill for the long-term care facility and the placement agency? First and most importantly, Medicare does not pay for long-term care anywhere.

So with that, let's address the expense of a long-term care facility. Individuals who have previously purchased long-term care insurance need to have their policy reviewed early because terms and conditions greatly vary from policy to policy and company to company. Some policies only cover long-term care if it is provided in home, while others will only cover the individual if placed in a long-term care facility.

I really encourage you to find out whether your parent has long-term care insurance way before they need it. Make contact with the policy provider to gain all the information. Policies have their own language so learn how the coverage works for your parent. Be aware that the insurance money never covers the entire bill, so be prepared to pay out of pocket for the remainder.

If there is no long-term care insurance, the cost is either paid by the individual or by the family.

Medicaid does pay for some facilities, but one has to qualify for it by making application. Speak to a social worker at the hospital or nursing facility as soon as possible to find out how to begin the process; it can take some time, and many papers need to be submitted prior to acceptance.

The cost of long-term care can be very costly, and in some situations, reaching upwards of $12,000 per month, so do your homework. If your parent has a house, that might be their greatest asset. Hard as it may be, seriously consider selling the house to pay for their long-term care needs.

Now let's look at the final question: Who pays the referral agency you hire to help find a place for Mom/Dad? Most referral agencies are paid their fee by the facility where you place your parent. In the event your parent is on Medicaid, which is a government assistance program, the placement fee is paid by your parent or the family. It is always wise to ask the referral agency what the cost and fees are *before* you hire it to show you around.

Just a quick tidbit of information to know ahead of time: An *intake assessment* is usually taken before any placement is made. The fee for this service can range from $250 to $400. The intake assessment is done either by a private nurse or someone from the new facility where your parent is moving. The assessor will set up a time to visit your parent to assess their true needs and abilities, and to determine whether the new facility would be a good fit for them. When that is completed, the findings will be returned to the new facility and will determine the real cost of the care. Make sure to ask about the *entrance fee* because it can cost a couple of thousand dollars upfront.

HELPFUL TIP 12

Don't hesitate to ask questions if needed for clarification. Finding the benefits that will best support your parent will, in turn, benefit you.

CHAPTER 13

LEANING IN

"In my deepest, darkest moments, what really got me through was a prayer. Sometimes my prayer was 'Help me.' Sometimes a prayer was 'Thank you.' What I've discovered is that intimate connection and communication with my creator will always get me through because I know my support, my help, is just a prayer away."

— Iyanla Vanzant

On this journey of caring for your parent, recognize that there will come times of great fatigue and even confusion coupled with frustration. You will need to lean in and find strength and encouragement to help you continue on. I found myself at this point with my *own* family, and that is when I began to remember something I read much earlier in life when I was searching for encouragement: "When I am weak, God is strong."

> "Even youths grow tired and weary, and young men/women stumble and fall; but those who hope in the Lord will renew their strength. They will soar on wings like eagles; they will run and not grow weary and they shall walk and not be faint."
>
> — Isaiah 40:30-31

We do get tired and weary at times, but I found my strength and much encouragement through the supportive words and promises found in the Holy Bible. Did you know the Bible is the inspired word of God, and it contains *His* love letters to you and me?

> "Come to me all who are weary and heavy-laden, and I will give you rest. Take my yoke upon you, and learn from me, for I am gentle and humble in heart; and you shall find rest for your souls. For my yoke is easy and my load is light."
>
> — Matthew 11:28-30

SEARCHING FOR THE ANSWERS

We face many challenges during our lives, and at times, questions go unanswered. Many of our questions are directed at God in hope of finding the answer. For instance: Where is God when I am hurting? Why did my child pass away so young? Why did my parent die at the hand of carelessness? Does God even care?

There are so many reasons why things happen the way they do. I don't claim to have the answers, though sometimes I wish I did so I could understand better myself why things happen the way they do. Sometimes life is a mystery, but what I do know is this: God loves. *Yes, God loves.* He loves us; that means *you* and *me,* and he *does* care.

Some might think of God as being like Santa Claus—obligated to give us everything on our wish list—or that prayer and God operate something like a gumball machine…quarter in, gumball out; quick prayer up and quick answer down. God does not always work that way. He is sovereign. The truth is that God loves us and wants us to reach out and receive the love He has for us.

God's love is *free* with no strings attached. God offers His love to all, and His grace is enough for each one of us. I have found His love to be full and intoxicating. I have personal experience with God's love and presence in my life, and it has sustained me for the past forty-one years. During an illness, loss, and disappointment, I have found that God does not always fix the problem, heal the illness, or stop my loved one from dying, *but* I have come to understand that *He* can handle it all, not me.

God gives me peace that passes all understanding, even when there is no human way out of the storm. He gives me grace when the situation is ugly, painful, and confusing. He has become *my* rock when the waves of life have crashed over me, wanting to drown me. He *is* my hope.

"I look to the hills where does my help come from, my help comes from the Lord, the maker of heaven and earth."

— Psalm 121:1-2

I have come to realize some things are just out of my hands or control. Depression, disappointment, and despair will all come our way at times, but God is not the author of them. He also is not the author of confusion, so when it comes my way, I choose to recognize it for what it is and reach for the Lord of peace. *Life is hard, but God is good.*

WALKING WITH GOD

What does it mean to walk with God? Jeff Vanderstelt, one of the great theologians, puts it this way in his book, *Saturate: Being Disciples of Jesus in the Everyday Stuff of Life*:

It is the ongoing process of submitting all of life to Jesus, and seeing him saturate your entire life and world with his presence and power. It's a process of daily growing in your awareness of your need for him in the everyday stuff of life. It is walking with Jesus, being filled with Jesus, and being led by Jesus in every place and in every way.

FINDING FAITH

The Bible says:

> "For God so loved the world that He sent His only Son" (John 3:16).
>
> It is only through Jesus that we can be right with God, our Heavenly Father. When Jesus died on the cross, He took away our sins and rebellion; He became *the bridge* so we are no longer separated from God. "We have peace with God through our Lord Jesus Christ" (Romans 5:1).

Throughout the Bible, Jesus offers forgiveness and eternal life as a free gift that no one can earn or buy, so no one can boast that he did it himself. This means that you no longer have to strive to be good enough or do certain rituals or tasks to receive this gift. It's called *grace.* With a simple heartfelt prayer to Jesus, the gift of forgiveness and eternal life can be yours.

In his book *The Case for Christ*, Lee Strobel states that making the decision to follow Christ is as simple as this: *Receive + Believe = Become.*

This is how God showed His love among us. "He sent his one and only Son into the world that we might live through him" (1 John 4:9).

By *receiving* the gift Jesus is offering and *believing* in Him, each one of us "*become* children of God" (John1:12). "[I]f you confess with your mouth the Lord Jesus and believe in your heart that God has raised Him from the dead, you will be saved" (Romans 10:9).

You must trust Jesus Christ and receive Him by personal invitation. You need to invite Him into your life. What that means is simply to believe He is who He claims to be and to receive the love He has for you. To invite Him into your life means to talk to Jesus and personally ask Him in. This conversation is called prayer, and it can be done anywhere and at any time, either out loud or silently.

The Bible says: "Behold, I stand at the door and knock. If anyone hears my voice and opens the door, I will come in to him and dine with him, and he with me" (Revelation 3:20).

Will you take a chance and ask Him in? Come find *peace and rest* for your soul, and unspeakable *joy.* I invite you to take a step of faith by repeating this simple prayer:

> Dear Lord Jesus,
> I know I have sin in my life and I need Your forgiveness.
> I want to turn from my sinful nature and follow You instead.
> Please forgive me.
> I believe You died on the cross to pay the cost for my sin.
> I thank You for loving me.
> I invite You to come live in me and my life today.
> In Your name, Amen.

Take a minute to jot down your signature below and date it. *He* has been waiting for you for such a long time!

Signature: ______________________________

Date: ______________________________

I am so thrilled you took this step! Go tell somebody about it, or if you would like to contact me to let me know, I will rejoice with you.

"You will seek me and find me when you seek
me with all your heart."

— Jeremiah 29:13

If you are not quite ready to receive the gift of salvation at this time, I hope you will give it some thought and consideration and ask God to make Himself real to you.

SPIRITUAL SUPPORT

Let me encourage you, in your walk of faith, by recommending that you find and listen to a good Christian radio station. The music is encouraging and very uplifting. In addition to music, these stations broadcast programs during the day with topics pertinent to singles, family, children, and everyday life. These programs contain very practical and educational information, and at times, they can be rather entertaining.

Grab your computer and look online for some of the churches in your area. Listen to the online messages or Sunday services to find spiritual support. Christian television is yet another source of education and information with daily movies, biblical teachings, and prayer.

Getting yourself plugged into a fellowship/church community is one of the very best ways to connect, and it will encourage you through the tough times that may lay ahead. By doing so, you will begin to grow in your relationship with God, the Father, and Jesus Christ, His son. The body of Christ (the Church) is there to uplift you in spirit and in prayer. Don't be afraid to let your fellow Christians know you need some encouragement, and when you are ready, let them into your life.

FINDING ENCOURAGEMENT

Find time in your day to open up the Bible and read. Begin with ten minutes and then increase the time as you can. You will draw great strength and understanding through the Word of God by doing so. To help encourage you, I have taken the time to jot down some of my favorite Bible verses, which, over time, have brought me great comfort and encouragement.

Write your favorite verses down on notecards and put them in your pocket to build yourself up. Notecards can be taped to the bathroom mirror, kitchen window over the sink, the refrigerator door, or even the car's glove box. Let your mind pore over the words daily and you will feel the love and compassion the Lord has for you in your life.

Practice these verses daily and they will make a big difference in the way you feel and think. Reach for the Holy Bible (I personally enjoy the New International Version), and read through the Gospel of John. Learn and memorize all you can; then read it again.

- "For God so loved the world that He gave His one and only Son." (John 3:16)

- "This is how God showed His love among us: He sent his one and only Son into the world that we might live through Him." (1 John 4:9)
- "I pray that out of His glorious riches He may strengthen you." (Ephesians 3:16-21)
- "Be still, and know that I am God." (Psalm 46:10)
- "Peace I leave you; my peace I give to you." (John 14:27)
- "Mercy in times of trouble." (Psalm 6:1-9)
- "The Lord is a refuge for the oppressed, and a strong hold in times of trouble." (Psalm 9:9-10)
- "Ever present help in times of trouble." (Psalm 46:1-3)
- "But when the kindness and love of God our Savior appeared, He saved us, not because of righteous things we had done, but because of His mercy. He saved us through the washing of rebirth and renewal by the Holy Spirit, whom he poured out on us generously through Jesus Christ our Savior, so that, having been justified by His grace, we might become heirs having the hope of eternal life." (Titus 3:4-7)
- "But I trust in your unfailing love…for He has been good to me." (Psalm 13:5-6)
- "He said to them, "Come with me by yourselves to a quiet place and get some rest." (Mark 6:31)
- "Because of the Lord's great love we are not consumed, for his compassions never fail. They are new every morning; great is your faithfulness." (Lamentations 3:22-23)
- "Therefore, if anyone is in Christ, he is a new creation; the old has gone, the new has come." (2 Corinthians 5:17)

With hundreds of books about religion on the market today, I would encourage you to pick up a copy of Lee Strobel's book, *The Case for Christ*, which offers a journalist's personal investigation of the evidence for Jesus; then you can cast your own verdict.

> "May the God of hope fill you with all joy and peace as you trust in Him, so that you may overflow with hope by the power of the Holy Spirit."
>
> — Romans 15:13

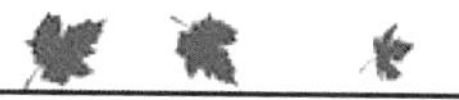

HELPFUL TIP 13

If you are thirsty and hungry and nothing seems to satisfy, I believe the Lord Jesus Christ is calling. Do not ignore him, but embrace the call by being excited that the God of the Universe is trying to get your attention.

God stands at the door and knocks. Have the courage to let Him in. There is hope and rest for you there.

CHAPTER 14

MOVING DAD

"Stop the world—I want to get off!"

— Unknown

DIFFICULT DECISIONS

My husband's and my decision to move my father-in-law into a nursing home was not an easy one. Honoring Dad's request to be cared for at home sounded reasonable at first, and because of his finances, it seemed doable. But then the information about in-home care, assisted living facilities, private adult family homes, nursing homes, and long-term care all seemed to jumble together inside my head.

Almost hourly, I found myself contemplating the pros and cons of each option of care that might best suit Dad's needs. One minute I was sure he could stay in the comfort of his home and all we would need would be a live-in caregiver, someone to do everything I had been doing for Dad for the past five weeks. But then I would return to the reality of the weariness in my mind and body.

How soon I had forgotten about the night before, when Dad had tried to get out of bed on his own and fallen to his knees; it had taken my husband Larry and me both to get him back into bed for the second time. Or what about the 4:30 a.m. bowel movement that took both of us to move Dad from the bed to the bedside commode just three feet away and back again? What about the cleanup and barrier cream that needed to be applied to those dark and private places? You do what needs to be done, but there comes a time when you need to recognize that the need is greater than what you can handle or provide.

Another major issue of consideration was neither the toilet nor shower in the master bathroom or second bathroom were accessible due to the lack of room for a wheelchair and an assistant. Dad's legs no longer wanted to support him so it became a chore to move him. With his weight over 215 pounds, I found him physically hard to handle, and even with the occasional help from my husband, the task became too overwhelming. I knew if we didn't do something very soon to change Dad's level of care, one of us could get physically injured. It was time to make a very tough decision.

In my estimation, it would take two strong caregivers to care for Dad around the clock if he were to stay at home, and at the approximate rate of $30 per hour per caregiver. Or we could possibly hire one strong caregiver every eight hours and bring in a Hoyer

Lift. Dad's home had been a great size for him and Mom when she was alive, but adding additional people into it, plus the wheelchair and all the other needed equipment, made the place a bit more cramped.

As much as we wanted Dad to be able to stay in his home, we knew there was no way to continue the way we were. For five days, I searched for an alternative solution to Dad's situation and his escalating care needs. During those days, I was immersed in twenty-four-hour thoughts and agony.

With so many options available, I thought it would be easy in the beginning. Now, with Dad's needs changing every couple of days, I quickly found my options narrowing. With his pain level rising came more medication; then came his inability to shower or toilet himself.

One morning at dawn, he tried to get out of bed and slid to the floor. I flew to his bedside and realized I couldn't get him back in bed on my own. Uninjured except for his pride, Dad just sat there while I phoned my husband for help. While my husband drove to our rescue, I placed two pillows on the floor, one for Dad and one for me. I laid him down to rest and covered him with a blanket. I then placed my head down to rest but kept one eye open on Dad. When my husband arrived, it took both of us to get Dad back on the bed.

Within the next forty-eight hours, we finally decided the situation needed to change and very quickly. We no longer had a choice; we knew it was time to move Dad to a nursing home. After exhausting all other options, including placement in an adult family home, we began looking for long-term care at an SNF that could best care for him full-time.

GUILT, SADNESS, AND FAILURE

This decision created a sense of intense guilt, sadness, and failure within me, yet it was intertwined with a sense of relief you can only understand once you have experienced it. There are times when hard choices need to be made—choices that are the *right* choices for the ones you love.

Dad's attitude toward life was slipping fast. He was becoming agitated and very irritable with everyone around him, and I sensed extreme anger rumbling just below the surface of his skin. Was that anger really directed at us, the people who loved him, or was it against the fear he felt knowing he was really losing the battle to survive? The independence he once knew was now being taken away, and others were making all the decisions for him. I sensed his fear and lack of control, and he did too, which horrified him. Fortunately, Dad had taken care of his directives and delegations of power years before, which eased some of the stress for our family during this extremely difficult time.

Settling Dad in at the SNF was a whole other story. On the outside, I was feeling relief, but on the inside, I was terrified! Had we made the right decision or were we premature? Would his needs be met? Had we found the best place for him? What if the SNF didn't give him the care *we* were able to give him? Would he be treated well?

We had heard horror stories about nursing homes over the years (and you probably have too). In my work helping others, I have personally observed less than adequate care conditions in certain facilities that made me uneasy. Those facilities fueled my own concerns and fears about placing Dad *anywhere*. Keeping all of this in mind, we felt satisfied that the facility we chose would provide the best of care for Dad.

EARLY GRIEF

As I now look back, I can see that grief was a large component during this time with Dad, although I wasn't able to see it then due to the stress and exhaustion. Wikipedia defines "grief" as: A multifaceted response to loss, particularly to the loss of someone or something that has died, to which a bond or affection was formed.

Another definition of grief (from griefrecoverymethod.com) says, "Grief is the normal emotional reaction to loss or change of any kind. Of itself, grief is neither a pathological condition nor a personality disorder. Grief is the conflicting feelings caused by the end of, or change in, a familiar pattern of behavior."

The following statement was enclosed in a thank you note I received from a woman who had recently attended one of the Care Conferences I held in Shoreline, Washington. That day's topics were "Caring for an Ill Loved One" and "Dementia."

> The written material I received at your latest Care Conference in Shoreline has been such a help for reference. As recently as yesterday I referred to it and realized that the sadness I feel so often is a part of the grief process. I've always believed grief follows after you've lost someone. I learned that grief can be experienced while in the process of losing someone and expe-

> riencing the changes that person is going through as well as the changes you (the spouse/caregiver) are personally facing.

This note affirmed what I have been teaching others about the experiences of grief and loss. Grief begins earlier than people may recognize, often long before your loved one passes. This was the case for me when we realized we had to move Dad and that the road for him was approaching its end.

HELPFUL TIP 14

I encourage you to make the time to read through Chapter 17: Processing Grief, before your loved one passes. You and your family will find helpful tools and insights as you journey through this tender season. Remember the process of grief can occur at any time.

CHAPTER 15
MAKING FUNERAL ARRANGEMENTS

"Plans are nothing; planning is everything."

— Dwight D. Eisenhower

Asking your parent questions regarding their funeral arrangements may seem rather cold and prohibitive, but when done with care and respect, it will provide much needed information and take speculation out of the equation.

In the next section, I have posed important questions that need to be answered. Many times, the spouse is well aware of the funeral arrangements since the arrangements are often made together by both spouses. In the event your parent is unwilling or physically unable to answer the following questions, be sure to schedule a time to meet with your other parent to get your questions answered. The more information you have gathered before your loved one passes away, the easier it will be on you and your family when that time *does* come.

I have modified an exercise I have used in some of my seminars to help you capture some of your parent's final wishes and requests. If possible, help them answer the following questions. If they are no longer able to answer the questions, possibly you or your family members may be able to help. These questions will outline the format for your parent's funeral/burial service. Remember to bring this information with you when you meet with the officiate of the service because it will be a great tool as he or she works together with you in creating your loved one's service.

FUNERAL ARRANGEMENTS

Where I want the service: ______________________________

Who will officiate: ______________________________

I want the focus to be: ______________________________

Special Readings: ______________________________

Favorite Scripture: ______________________________

Favorite Verses: ______________________________

Special Music: ______________________________

Favorite Hymns: ______________________________

Musician: ______________________________________

Soloist: ______________________________________

Favorite Flowers: ______________________________

I would like a memorial fund set up for: ______________

Please notify the following people/organizations upon my death:

____

____

____

____

____

____

Have any prior funeral arrangements been made, and if so, where?

____

____

Burial or Cremation: ____________________________

Who made the arrangements and when?

____

____

Where is this information about the funeral arrangements located?

____

____

Who is to be called to receive the body at the time of death?

____

____

INTERMENT vs. INURNMENT

Death may occur at any time, as you know. It can happen early in the morning or in the dark of night; death ticks its own clock. Hopefully, there is time ahead to prepare and make final arrangements, but often, there are circumstances when death occurs far sooner than was anticipated, in which case arrangements will have to be made rather quickly.

Here are some terms that are frequently used during the process of making final arrangements with a funeral home or for a service. It would serve you well to be familiar with some of this terminology.

Interment/Inurnment cost has to do with all the expenses associated with the preparation of an individual's remains after he or she has passed away, including the casket, or an urn.

Interment means to bury a deceased body in the earth in a grave or tomb. *Inurnment* is the placing of one cremated in an urn. The cost of these services will greatly vary depending upon the choices you and your family select. So the question *is* will it be a burial or will it be a cremation? Both are good choices.

Did you know there are several different types of locations in which to place the remains of your loved one? A body and casket or cremated remains may be buried in a grave or tomb, and can also be released at sea. Cremated remains can be placed in a *niche*, which is a hollow place in a wall exclusively for urns. *Mausoleums* are either public or private buildings specially designed to receive entombments as a permanent above-ground resting place for the dead. And finally, *columbariums* are a structure of vaults lined with recesses for urns containing cremated remains.

Hopefully, your parent has previously discussed this matter with you and you are well aware of their final arrangements and wishes. In the event these arrangements have been made and were paid for in advance, I suggest you follow your parent's plan. If there is still time before your parent passes away, take some time to review the documents and paperwork for these arrangements.

See whether there is still money owing for these arrangements and whether additional charges and fees will be upcoming. Make a phone call to the funeral home or agency where these arrangements were made and introduce yourself to the director or staff. Do not hesitate to ask them any questions you may have so you can have a clear understanding of what services and options are offered. Be sure to ask for the phone number to call when your parent does pass away and ask what steps you will need to take thereafter.

One important question is to find out whether there is a family plot or crypt already purchased and whether there is enough room in it for your parent. Is this where your parent/loved one would want to be laid to rest? Ask your family members if you don't know the answers to these questions.

If there are no final arrangements in place for your parent after they pass away, now is the time to begin making some plans. Money is usually a major factor. Burials are always more expensive than cremation. With a burial, a casket (not a coffin), needs to be purchased as well as a burial plot. If there is an existing family burial plot, the cost is lessened, but there are additional fees and charges associated with it, so be sure to ask. Purchasing space in a mausoleum, a niche, or any of the previously mentioned options above will also greatly vary in cost. Cremated remains can be buried or scattered, but be informed of the legalities. Cremation for some is more practical and a better economical choice, so be mindful of all your options before choosing.

I would advise you to start taking steps toward these decisions well before the death of your parent becomes imminent. If you recall, earlier in this book we discussed the topic of stress and what it does to your body and brain. Take the time to research and make informed decisions while your body and brain are rested and not under demand.

Start your search by contacting the local funeral services and funeral homes in your area and begin asking questions. Make it a point to contact two or three others to make a better informed assessment. Remember to ask the same questions of each and write down their answers so you can have an even comparison at the end.

A word of caution to the wise: Do not get caught up in the many funeral packages some of these funeral homes offer. Avoid being talked into purchasing more than you need and can afford. Remember, you and your family are very vulnerable at this point, so do not feel guilty if you do not purchase the "Eternal, Forever Remembered, Most Dearly Beloved Package" (if you understand my drift). Buy only what you need and can afford. Be sure to ask about any hidden fees and additional charges that have not been previously mentioned up front or in your discussions when making arrangements.

SERVICES FOR YOUR PARENT

For the past eighteen years, I have worked with many families, helping them craft their loved ones' final plans and to close the final chapter of their lives. There are many ways to put to rest and celebrate the life of your parent so let's explore a few options.

What is a memorial?

A memorial is a service to acknowledge a person's life publically so that family and friends can have closure and share memories and experiences. Over the last 10-15 years, memorials have been popularly referred to as "Celebrations of Life," and they can be held just about anywhere and are no longer restricted to churches or funeral homes. For this type of service, a body or casket is usually not present.

What is a funeral?

A funeral is a service very similar to a memorial service that occurs in a funeral home or place of worship and involves having the casket on site, sometimes for viewing purposes, depending on whether the event is open or closed casket. Some funeral services occur in the chapel on the premises of the cemetery where the person will be laid to rest. Other funeral services occur at a place of worship followed by burial at a cemetery. After the funeral service, there is a procession in which the casket is transported to the cemetery for burial with family and friends, at which time the person's body is laid to rest.

What is a graveside service?

A graveside service is a service that occurs directly at the gravesite where a person will be laid to rest. This service occurs in a cemetery and involves the process of lowering the casket into the ground. A graveside service could also include the placement of an urn with the ashes of your loved one, or the placement of remains into a mausoleum wall. Usually, an officiate hosts the event. It can be a short type of service that is open-ended in terms of structure. For example, it may be a religious service with prayers where a eulogy is read, or it might be a quiet time for family and friends to reflect and say their final farewell to their loved ones, or it could be both.

Who officiates at these type of events?

You may not know this, but *anyone* can officiate a memorial or funeral service, and that includes you or another family member. Funeral homes can also provide an officiate. The only restrictions are those mandated by places of worship. Most people, after losing a loved one, are seeking spiritual guidance and support, so I encourage you either to seek guidance from your own pastor or clergy, or the pastor or clergy of your parent if your parent participated in a place of worship. Whether or not you attend a place of worship, you can still contact one to seek assistance.

The tone and experience of the service you plan, regardless of location, is totally up to you. I am suggesting that you use the experience to create a positive, uplifting celebration of life that exemplifies the personal attributes of your loved one, despite your loved one's human foibles. This is an opportunity for remembrance and closure.

Remember, *respect, honor, and dignity....*

Regardless of whom you choose to officiate, here are some *ideas to help celebrate the life of your loved one:*

1. Release individual balloons or a bouquet of colored balloons at the beach, park, or at a location that is special to the family or individual.
2. Release white doves after your service to symbolize the releasing of the human spirit from earth to heaven.
3. Place a packet of forget-me-not seeds inside the funeral/memorial program.
4. Tell others in lieu of flowers: "Please donate to your/my parent's favorite charity."

Maybe you have some other creative ideas in mind. Let yourself explore these ideas and share your thoughts with family members. Your creativity is limitless.

On a different note, once the service of your parent is over, you may begin to realize a lot of work still lies ahead to finalize your parent's affairs. This may include the sale of a home, the distribution of belongings and assets, and other surfacing tasks. Give yourself grace as you begin to walk into these final tasks and don't forget to *breathe.*

HELPFUL TIP 15

If you are able, get information from your parent about their final wishes. Asking good questions makes for good answers. There are many options with variable costs. Be sure to stay within your financial means.

CHAPTER 16

END-OF-LIFE ISSUES

"But our machines have now been running seventy or eighty years, and we must expect that, worn as they are, here a pivot, there a wheel, now a pinion, next a spring, will be giving way; and however we may tinker them up for a while all will at length surcease motion."

— Thomas Jefferson to John Adams, July 5, 1814

Many years ago, when I first began volunteering at my church as the care team leader, I paid a visit to one of our home-bound members. Her name was Sophia, and I soon learned she was battling pancreatic cancer. She was still living in her own home, but without the assistance of her two loving and dedicated daughters with their around-the-clock care, she would not have been able to make it on her own.

When I met Sophia on that first visit, she reminded me so much of my own mother. She was from Hungary, and with her beautiful smile, accent, and European ways, I was soon taken in. Her adult daughters were a delight as well; with open arms, they all welcomed me and invited me into their tumultuous world.

It was summertime, so each day sent the thermometer climbing. This was one of the warmest summers I had seen in Seattle in many years. My first couple of visits, I found Sophia dressed in normal daily attire, seated on the couch and enjoying a fresh bowl of cut-up fruit. We would converse about the weather, family, and life in Europe. On occasion, she would insist on me sharing her bowl of fruit, which I finally succumbed to doing. I felt she needed the nourishment more than I, but when her fork poked my cheek, I joyfully took a bite. I think it was her way of saying, "I'm glad you're here; you are one of us." It made me grin, and at times even chuckle, as I looked at her daughters who were smiling and then back into Sophia's warm and loving eyes.

Time moved quickly in Sophia's life. One day she was managing, and then in a manner of just a few days, immense pain took over. Sophia was still ambulatory, but in my eyes, she should *not* have been. She would manage to get to the couch, her bed, and the toilet with the aid of her daughters, but it was a painful endeavor, and to observe it was almost as painful.

By the second week, Sophia was no longer able or interested in eating because the pain in her abdomen was so great. When I called the family to check in, I was informed by one of her daughters that Sophia had cried out in pain most of the night before. The pain medication that had previously been prescribed was no longer helping. The daughter was so at a loss that she told me she had debated taking her mother to the emergency room, but then she decided to call the doctor's office first thing that morning. She was instructed to bring her mother into the office and was told that the emergency department would not have known what to do for Sophia had she taken her there.

So, rather confused but desperate, the daughter loaded her mother into the car and drove to the doctor's office. Upon their return home, I was informed that the doctor had prescribed new and different pain pills that were twice the size of the old ones. Sophia was already having trouble swallowing, so it was going to take a miracle to get these new jumbo pills down.

(Just a side note here: There are several different tricks to help make medication easier to swallow such as cutting pills in half, smashing them with the back of a spoon, dissolving them with a small amount of water or juice, or adding one to a spoonful of applesauce or pudding to make it palatable. *Be cautious here!* Not all medications *should be* taken broken apart. Many pills are time-released so cutting/crushing them and then administrating them in that fashion could be very harmful or even fatal. *Please,* consult with the doctor and pharmacist before doing so.)

Sophia's daughters and I had previously spoken about talking with the doctor to see whether he felt it was time to sign Sophia up for hospice. Observing her lack of abilities and poor health, it became very clear to me that it was time for a hospice team to step in. All that was needed now was the doctor's consent. I had voiced my concern and observations to Sophia's family, but when the matter was brought up to the doctor, it was a moot point. In my experience, it was a very apparent and appropriate referral. I had a very difficult time resting with the doctor's decision. I realized I wasn't family, so to debate the issue with the daughters was not my place, but I could gently lead and guide them to become advocates for their mother.

Families depend on doctors to call the shots and make most of the hard decisions because they believe doctors are best informed. I want to encourage families to begin to write down their questions ahead of time and then jot down the answers. If parents can't speak for themselves, then someone else must be their voice. Your parent may be too ill to think of some of the important questions to ask, so you and your family need to be ready. Don't be afraid to ask questions. The information you receive will be helpful to know.

I've been told that many times doctors don't like to assign hospice too early, but in my opinion, it's more often a little late. Generally, hospice is assigned when a patient has six months or less to live. It must be very difficult for doctors to have to inform patients that they have reached this stage and to realize they have done all they could and still it isn't enough. At this same juncture, it might be a good time to have your parent complete a Personal Value Statement, which is described in the following section.

PERSONAL VALUE STATEMENT

A Personal Value Statement communicates the personal thoughts and wishes one might have about their health and life. The form is mostly used when life expectancy is short. Questions include:

- Currently, how are you feeling about your health situation?

- Would you like to continue making your own decisions regarding your health?
- How do you feel about others making decisions for you?
- As end of life draws near, what would be most important to you?

While filling out this form is not mandatory, the process and questions empower your parent to participate in and voice their desires, and it can provide valuable insight for the family.

When my mother was in her last three months of life, I suggested she complete a Personal Value Statement for herself. I reminded her that my brother, who didn't visit that often, would probably like to know some of her thoughts and desires. My mother agreed, but she asked me to help her write it out due to her poor health and arthritic fingers. I was surprised by some of her answers to the questions, but I was faithful to write only the words she spoke without embellishment or censorship. I had her sign and date the statement to verify she had initiated the answers to the questions on the document. This is always a good practice.

I have asked permission from the families I coach and counsel to sit with their parent and fill in the answers if they would like. Many times, family members are too close so the ailing parent can't be totally honest with their true feelings from fear they may hurt someone's feelings or possibly be attacked or scrutinized for the way they really feel.

As end of life nears, it's always good to refer back to the Personal Value Statement and review it again. Things that weren't so important a month back are possibly now very important. As time becomes more limited, some hard requests may need to be honored. For example, maybe your parent no longer wants to have outside visitors and only wants to spend their time with family, holding them near.

You can find a copy of the Personal Value Statement in *The Personal Health Care Manual.* Share the completed Personal Value Statement with your parent's hospice team members so they can better honor your parent's requests. In the next section, we'll look more closely at hospice, but first, let me say: Hospice is a *wonderful* organization! Let me state that again: Hospice is a *wonderful* organization with many amazing and caring people!

HOSPICE

Hospice is considered the model for quality, compassionate care at the end of life. It provides expert medical care, pain management, and emotional and spiritual care individually tailored to each person's needs. When no more medical measures can be taken to cure an illness and life-limiting conditions exist, families can elect hospice to come on board. Again, hospice can only be assigned by a physician, so it is wise to ask whether it is time for hospice to step-in. Don't hesitate to bring it up with the doctor if he hasn't already. Help to be the advocate for your loved one when they can't advocate for themselves any longer. Remember, you see them a lot more than the doctor does.

Hospice offers care, comfort, and support for both patient and family. Usually, a five-person team, consisting of a physician, nurse, social worker, home health aide, and spiritual caregiver (chaplain), will be assigned to your loved one. This team will be involved in the support and care of each patient.

Who pays for hospice? It is available as a benefit under Medicare Part A. If your loved one isn't eligible for Medicare benefits yet, hospice might still be available. Contact your physician or call 1-800-MEDICARE (1-800-633-4227) for the Medicare handbook. Learn more about hospice by visiting some of the following websites or contacting them by phone:

National Hospice Palliative Care Organization (NHPCO):
www.hpco.org
www.caringinfo.org
www.caringinfo@nhpco.org
Consumer Helpline 1-800-658-8898

Contact your local hospital for the hospice organization in your area, and be sure to check with the insurance provider/Medicare to see what coverage is available. Remember, hospice becomes involved in the care of your parent only when the diagnosis for continued life is six months or less.

At this juncture, I would like to prepare you for some things that may lay ahead. The following information may be difficult for you to read, but I encourage you to read all of the way through until the end if you can, hard as it may be, because it will give you critical information that can actually shift your fear and responses to how you handle and assist in your loved one's passing. This information is a compilation of information used by Hospice itself.

PREPARING FOR APPROACHING DEATH

When a person enters the final stages of the dying process, two different dynamics are at work that are closely related. On the physical plane, the body begins the process of shutting down, which will end when all the physical systems cease to function. Usually, this is an orderly and undramatic progressive series of physical changes that are not medical emergencies requiring invasive interventions. These physical changes are a normal, natural way that the body prepares itself to stop, and the most appropriate kinds of responses are comfort-enhancing measures.

The other dynamic of the dying process is at work on the emotional-spiritual-mental plane, and it is a different kind of process. The "spirit" of the dying person begins the final process of releasing itself from the body, its immediate environment, and all attachments. This release also tends to follow its own path, which may include resolving whatever is unfinished of a practical nature and receiving permission to "let go" from family members. These "events" are the normal, natural way the spirit prepares to move from this existence into the next dimension of life. The most appropriate kinds of responses to the emotional-spiritual-mental changes are those that support and encourage this release and transition.

When a person's body is ready and wanting to stop, but the person is still unresolved or unreconciled over an important issue or with a significant relationship, the person may continue to live. Even though they may seem uncomfortable or debilitated, they may linger in order to finish whatever needs finishing. Likewise, when a person is emotionally, spiritually, and mentally resolved and ready for this release, but the body has not completed its final physical process, the person may continue to live until the physical shutdown is complete.

The experience we call death occurs when the body completes its natural process of shutting down, and the spirit completes its natural process of reconciling and finishing. These two processes need to happen in a way appropriate and unique to the dying person's values, beliefs, and lifestyle.

Therefore, as you seek to prepare yourself as this event approaches, the members of your hospice team want you to know what to expect and how to respond in ways that will help your loved one accomplish this transition with support, understanding, and ease. This is the great gift of love you have to offer your loved one as this moment approaches.

The physical, emotional, spiritual, and mental signs and symptoms of impending death that follow are offered to help you understand the natural kinds of things that may happen and how you can respond appropriately. Not all these signs and symptoms will occur with every person, nor will they occur in this particular sequence. Each person is unique and needs to do things in his or her own way. This is not the time to try to change your loved one, but a time to give full acceptance, support, and comfort.

The following signs and symptoms are indicative of how the body prepares itself for the final stage of life:

Coolness: The person's hands, arms, feet, and maybe legs may be increasingly cold to the touch and, at the same time, the color of the skin may change. The underside of the body may become darker. The skin may become mottled. This is a normal indication that the circulation is decreasing to the body's extremities and being reserved for the "most vital organs."

What you can do: Keep the person warm with a blanket. Electric blankets should not be used.

Sleeping: The person may spend an increasing amount of time sleeping and appear to be uncommunicative or unresponsive and at times be difficult to arouse. This normal change is due in part to changes in the body's metabolism.

What you can do: Sit with your loved one, hold their hand, do not shake or speak loudly, but speak softly and naturally. Plan to spend time with them during those times when they seem most alert/awake. Speak to them directly as you normally would, even though there may be no response. Never assume the person cannot hear since hearing is the last of the senses to be lost.

Disorientation: The person may seem to be confused about the time, place, and identity of people surrounding them, including close familiar people. This is also due in part to metabolic changes.

What you can do: Identify yourself by name as you enter rather than asking the person to guess who you are. Speak softly, clearly, and truthfully when you need to communicate something important to the patient's comfort such as "It's time to take your medicine," and explain reasons for the communication, such as "So you don't begin to hurt."

Incontinence: The person may lose control of bladder and/or bowel function as the muscles in that area begin to relax.

What you can do: Discuss with your hospice team what can be done to keep your loved one clean and comfortable.

Congestion: The person may have gurgling sounds coming from their chest or throat; these sounds may become very loud. This normal change is due to the decrease of fluid intake and an inability to cough up normal secretions. Suctioning usually only increases the secretions and causes sharp discomfort. The sound of the congestion does not indicate the onset of severe or new pain.

What you can do: Gently turn the person's head to the side and allow gravity to drain the secretions. You may also gently wipe the mouth with a moist cloth.

Physical Restlessness: The person may make restless and repetitive motions such as pulling at bed linen or clothing. This often happens and is due in part to the decrease of oxygen circulation to the brain and to the metabolic changes.

What you can do: Do not interfere with or try to restrain such motions. To have a calming effect, speak in a quiet, natural way, lightly massage the forehead, read to the person, or play some soothing music.

Fluid and Food Decrease: The person may have a decrease in appetite and thirst, wanting little or no food/fluid. The body will naturally begin to conserve energy that is expended on these tasks. Do not try to force food or drink into the person, or try to use guilt to manipulate them into eating or drinking something. To do so only makes the person much more uncomfortable.

What you can do: Small chips of ice, or frozen Gatorade or juice may be refreshing in the mouth. If the person is able to swallow, fluids may be given in small amounts by syringe (ask your hospice team for guidance). Glycerin swabs may keep the mouth and lips moist and comfortable. Lip balm/ChapStick may be applied to the lips. A cold moist washcloth on the forehead may also increase physical comfort.

Urine Decrease: The person's urine output normally decreases and may become "tea" colored or have an unusual odor. This is referred to as concentrated urine. This is due to the decreased fluid intake as well as decrease in circulation through the kidneys.

What you can do: Consult with your hospice team to determine whether there may be a need to insert or irrigate a catheter.

Breathing Pattern Changes: The person's regular breathing pattern may change with the onset of a different pace. One particular pattern consists of breathing irregularly (i.e., shallow breaths with periods of no breathing of 5-30 seconds and up to a full minute). This is called "Cheyne-Stokes" breathing. This person may also experience periods of rapid, shallow, pant-like breathing. These patterns are very common and indicate decrease in circulation in the internal organs.

What you can do: Elevating the head of the bed and/or turning the person on their side may bring comfort. Hold their hand. Speak gently.

OTHER SIGNS AND SYMPTOMS

Withdrawal: The person may seem unresponsive, withdrawn, or in a comatose-like state. This indicates preparation for release, detaching from surroundings and relationships, and the beginning of "letting go."

What you can do: Since hearing remains all the way to the end, speak to your loved one in your normal voice. Identify yourself by name when you speak. Hold their hand. Say whatever you need to say that will help the person "let go."

Vision-Like Experiences: The person may speak or claim to have seen places not presently accessible to you. This does not indicate a hallucination or a drug reaction. The person is beginning to detach from this life and is being prepared for the transition so it will not be frightening.

What you can do: Do not contradict, explain away, belittle, or argue about what the person claims to have seen or heard. Just because you can't see or hear it does not mean it's not real to your loved one. Affirm their experiences. They are normal and common. If they frighten your loved one, explain to them that they are normal.

Mental/Spiritual Restlessness: The person may perform repetitive and restless tasks. This may in part indicate that something is still unresolved or unfinished and is interfering with the "letting go" process. Your hospice team members will assist you in identifying what may be happening, and help you find ways to help the person find release from the tension and fear.

What you can do: Recall a favorite place or favorite experience the person enjoyed, read something comforting, play music, and give assurance that it is okay to "let go."

Decreased Socialization: The person may only want to be with a few people or even just one person. This is a sign of preparation for release and an affirming of who the support is most needed from in order to make an appropriate transition. If you are not a part of this "inner circle" at the end, it does not mean you are not a loved one or are unimportant. It means you have already fulfilled your task with your loved one and it is time for you to say "Goodbye."

What you can do: If you are a part of the final "inner circle" of support, the person needs your affirmation, support, and permission.

Unusual Communication: The person may make a seemingly "out of character" or non-sequitur statement, gesture, or request. This indicates that they are ready to say "Goodbye" and are "testing" you to see whether you are ready to let them go.

What you can do: Accept the moment as a beautiful gift when it is offered. Kiss, hug, hold, cry, and say whatever you most need to say.

Giving Permission: Giving permission to your loved one to "let go" without making them feel guilty for leaving or trying to keep them with you to meet your own needs can be difficult. A dying person will normally try to hold on (even though it brings prolonged discomfort) in order to be sure those left behind will be all right.

What you can do: Your ability to release the dying person from this concern and give them reassurance that it is all right to "let go" whenever they are ready is one of the greatest gifts you have to give your loved one at this time.

Saying Goodbye: When the person is ready to die and you are able to "let go," then it is time to say, "Goodbye." Saying "Goodbye" is your final gift of love to your loved one. It achieves closure and makes the final release possible.

What you can do: It may be helpful to lie in bed with them and then say everything you need to say, "I'm sorry for whatever I contributed to any tensions or difficulties in our relationship." It may also include saying, "Thank you for...."

Tears are a normal and natural part of saying "Goodbye." Tears do not need to be hidden from your loved one or apologized for. Tears express your love and help you let go.

The ending is the same for all; the final breath is taken, but life doesn't have to stop there. For many, their hope is that "to be absent from the body is to be present with the Lord." Regardless of your faith, it is normal to feel left behind, sad, relieved, and even grateful that it's finally over and that your parent isn't suffering anymore.

Grief is a process we each have to go through, but we don't have to go it alone. While you may already be experiencing some degree of grief and loss, now that your loved one is gone, you may experience a deeper level of grief. Remember to take some quiet time for yourself, or a nap if possible. Take a walk outside to get some fresh air even if it's only for ten minutes. Practice being thankful. Look at the beauty around you and try to take it in. It won't be easy, and probably, you won't want to, *but do it anyway.* Invite good friends to come for a visit or meet them for coffee. Let them know you would like their company that day. Start with little steps. Exercise is a great way to let go and reduce stress. If you have a membership, then go to the gym. If not, join one. Any type of physical activity will do you some good.

Give yourself a well-deserved pat on the back that you were brave enough to read through this entire section. While this content is difficult to acknowledge, it is very important information that will serve you and your family well when the time approaches. The next chapter will provide you with the help and encouragement you need at this next milestone of your journey.

HELPFUL TIP 16

The process of dying is as individual as each person on the planet. We each have a story, and our ending is as much a part of who we are, as who we used to be. Don't let it frighten you. Just learn to understand it.

CHAPTER 17

PROCESSING GRIEF

"Grief is a life-altering experience. It takes time."

— Unknown

It's natural to care for and love someone, and it's okay to let yourself become vulnerable for the sake of being loved in return. It is normal to grieve the loss of a spouse, parent, child, or even a friend. There is really no timeline for grief, and the journey is very individual. During your time of grief, try not to stay idle too long. Grief is a process and you can get stuck in it.

It's perfectly normal to have emotions and feel a sense of loss, and even a time of numbness. It's when those feelings never lift or give way that you should be concerned. Be sure to watch over the surviving parent and other family members and pay close attention to them. A word to the wise: Don't discount a friend or spouse if they share they are concerned about you. Remember, you are at risk too.

SAM'S STORY

A very tender story I occasionally share with others is about a young man I met while cruising through the beautiful islands of the South Pacific aboard an elegant Holland America Cruise ship. It must have been 3:00 or 4:00 a.m. and I had been tossing and turning all night. My husband Larry and I were on day fourteen of our thirty-day cruise through the Polynesian Islands with Micronesia added in as a bonus. Gayle, one of our good friends, had decided to join us on this adventurous trip of new discovery and life on the high seas, and all was going well so far. The trip even afforded plenty of sun and warmth to go around, which I so enjoyed.

After hearing the prompts to arise and quieting my inner whining due to lack of sleep, I finally rose to my feet. Mornings have always been difficult for me, even as a kid. My eyes didn't seem to focus right and my body always rebelled, but nonetheless, I got up and out of bed.

My first thought was to grab my computer and the manuscript of this book and make my way up to the lido deck of this beautiful and pristine Holland America ship. I tiptoed over and grabbed my clothes and room key from the stand so as not to wake my husband. Then I heard him whisper, "You're up rather early." I whispered back, "I'm heading to the lido deck to work on my book." What I really wanted to say was "I can't believe it, but I'm up and the Lord really wants me to go to the lido deck now and work on my book." Instead of telling me I must be crazy to be up at such an early hour, Larry gently murmured in a soft and gentle voice, "Good for you..." as he drifted back to sleep.

I knew there would be hot coffee and a warm, peaceful atmosphere waiting for me, and I trusted the lights would already be on as I made my way up the six flights.

As the elevator doors opened, I sauntered down to the aft of the ship toward the coffee and felt the familiarity of the ship once again. It was so comfortable and cozy with the same feeling of warmth as my home. We have traveled so many times on Holland America that the ships have become familiar to us, even though each is unique. My husband and I enjoy this uniqueness, and we can always find one another if we choose to split up for separate activities during the day.

Larry enjoys the library, history lectures, the game of Sudoku, and walking the promenade deck with earbuds while listening to books on tape. I, in turn, enjoy the sun and its warmth. If I could store the sun's heat and warmth and bring it back home to the Pacific Northwest with me, I most certainly would. My body runs a bit cool in temperature, but my prayer is that my heart will always stay warm inside and out, and this morning was no different. I wasn't quite sure what the day had in store for me or how productive I would be at this hour of the morning, but I took a chance anyway.

As I approached the coffee area, I saw I was the only soul to be found. I thought there had to be at least one person who was awake besides me on this vessel. As I poured my first steamy cup of coffee, a young Indonesian steward named Sam approached with a warm smile and joyful morning greeting. He inquired why I was up so early as he noticed my laptop, legal pad, and spiral notebook in tow.

We began to chat and I shared what I was up to. I spoke briefly about how many Americans are dealing with aging parents and talked a bit about my journey with my own family. He listened quietly, although I wasn't sure whether he fully understood what I was saying. Sam was young, lean, and soft-spoken. He waited patiently as I ended my spiel, and then he began to tell me his story.

He began with "You make me remember." His speech was soft and quiet. He had a beautiful smile as his story unfolded. His story was like so many stories I've heard before while doing my work. It doesn't matter where I am in this world (literally) or what I'm in the middle of, I love to hear people's stories. That this man was allowing himself to be vulnerable with me was an honor. Life can be so busy, and it seems as though we don't have enough time to slow down and really listen to people, but the truth is, we actually do have time. One of the biggest gifts we can give someone is our time.

Sam spoke about his family in Indonesia and the loss of his parents. His father's death was recent and Sam's heart was sad that he had been unable to be at his father's side at the time of his death. I could feel the sadness in his heart and could sympathize so much with his pain. I understood how people grieving loss often repeatedly re-live the scenario of the event and the accompanying feeling of sadness because nothing they can do will change or fix the events. I could actually see Sam replaying the tape over and over again in his head as he spoke. He was frustrated that he hadn't been there for his father.

How do you offer comfort to someone in a situation like that? I listened intently and practiced the art of being present that we talked about in Chapter 2. I was not looking for answers to fix him; I was just *really* listening. Often, people become uncomfortable when conversations become emotional, but rather than trying to divert or leave situations that make you feel uncomfortable, I encourage you not to run away but to step gently into them. This is where comfort can be found.

We talked for six minutes or so. I mentioned the hope I have within my life. I spoke of my need for prayer and the Lord's promise never to leave or forsake me, even in the midst of despair. I told Sam that even though his pain would be there for a while, it would also stretch him and even give him compassion for someone who might in turn need him as he continued to travel. I tenderly reached out, touched his shoulder, and told him I would be praying for him. With that, a warm smile crossed his lips.

Our conversation came to an end as we each returned to our jobs at hand, I with my book and he with his work. I was so grateful to be a part of this young man's morning, and I hope he felt the same. I will continue to pray for peace and comfort for him, and I trust in time he too will be able to move forward from the sting and pain of losing someone dear to his heart.

Grief is normal, natural, and healthy, as long as you don't stay there too long. Below you will find information about the "Stages of Grief" that can help you understand the process of experiencing grief. You may relate to some of these stages, not necessarily in the order shown on the following page.

STAGES OF GRIEF

In my experience working with families who have loved ones who are dying, the process of going through the stages of grief are unique to each person. While some people may already have accepted the finality of the situation, others may be *stuck* in one area of the cycle of grief. There is no wrong way to grieve. It is important, too, to recognize that your loved one began their grief process the day they received their diagnosis, so they entered the grief process long before you did.

Through the years, I have come to realize that *grief* has many faces, and it is not just reserved for funerals. Many times, grief begins before we recognize what it is. Nor is grief just related to death; it can be experienced in many other areas of life. We expect it when there is a loss of life, but it can also occur when there is a loss of a job, promotion, relationship, or even a dream. We grieve when our children come home from school and tell us no one played with them at recess. We also grieve when our good friends move away or our children move away to college, even though it's for their own good. We human beings grieve.

Nine months before my mom passed away, I attended a class on grief. I had signed up with the intention to be better prepared to help others, not realizing that *my* heart would be the first to receive aid. I will never forget the very first night of class. I arrived about fifteen minutes late, panting like a thirsty dog, sweat on my brow and under my arms, body and mind exhausted, with my nerves frayed, asking myself, "Why am I *even* here?"

My mom's health was teetering, and there had been days I thought would be her last. I nicknamed her the "Energizer Bunny." She continued to rebound from death's door to life countless times, which seemed to jerk my emotions *every single time.* Hence, emotional exhaustion began. I guess if I didn't choose to love her so much and to care, it wouldn't have fazed me. Love can hurt, *but* it's worth it.

This particular day was heaped with Mom's needs and pending crisis. The one and only assignment given for the class was to return to class the next day with a completed timeline. The instructions were to create our personal timeline beginning at some monumental time in our lives, up to the current date. The monumental time could be a graduation, wedding, or the birth of a child, or it could include a negative event such as death or a traumatic event. We had to decide what the event was. From there, we were instructed to draw a line to the current date and then back-fill all the dates when loss had affected our lives.

In my mind, I was *refusing* to do the exercise. I reasoned that I was too exhausted and thought "Why does this really matter?" Later that evening, I was self-convicted by my poor attitude and began the homework. Much to my surprise, my timeline filled the page with a story—*my* story. I remembered all the events like they were yesterday, and I was amazed by how vivid the memories still were. I began to get a glimpse of the exercise's benefit.

Following is an example of my timeline just to get you started.

1997	flood, bridge, no mom
'98	mom's stroke, Gpa heart, Dad's cancer
'99	new cabin, Dad died
2000	El Salvador, breakdown
'01-'02	J. grad., J. college
'03	G.Jane died, A. grad., A. college, J. Africa
'04	puppies
'05	J. Canada
'06	JH. grad., JH. Arizona, Gma died
'07	D. grad., D.military, A. Boston
'08	Mom hospice
'09	mom lungs collapsed, mom died, D. Iraq, J. engaged

This exercise helped me understand why, at the time I was attending the class, my heart was so heavy. Each time my pen wrote another date on the timeline, I felt some of the events again. Tears came and I realized that with some events the grief was now gone, yet others were still needing healing.

Creating a timeline is an opportunity for personal reflection to see the highs and lows in our lives and to acknowledge them. Loss is seen in my timeline mixed in with the joy.

On a blank piece of paper, take a few minutes and begin to create your own timeline. If you need to work backwards, that's okay. You will be amazed by what you see. You will want to list the date, year, and just a word or two to serve as a personal reminder of each event or situation that brought on grief. Celebrate the good times you recall, but also recognize the sad times. Both need to be acknowledged. Keep in mind, this exercise is not meant for you to walk back into those sad times with the grief you once experienced, but rather to accept them as a time of loss. Perhaps, just maybe, *now* is *your* time to let go of the sadness and grief. I encourage you to take some time with this exercise and allow the hurt and pain that may still exist to finally heal. Prayer can change everything.

Occassionally, I glance back at my own personal timeline. I still have the original paper tucked inside a book to remind me of the victories won and the triumphs of overcoming those adversities in my life. It was a great snapshot of those twelve years, but it was also a healing tool so I could *finally* ask God to help me let go. My hope is that this exercise will also help *you* in the process of *your* grief.

COPING WITH GRIEF

After a loss, it's very easy to withdraw inside yourself and become introspective as you sort through your pain and memories and try to piece things together. Doing this is perfectly normal. But as the days pass, remember to continue to:

Eat, sleep, and breathe....

As you journey through your grief, don't be surprised by your own behavior. Grief may be ugly, and it can make people act out in ways that don't fit who they are. This also applies to family members. They may not exhibit the same manifestation of grief as you do. No sign of tears, no mourning, no anything. They return to their work/routine the very next day or two and seem unscathed by the loss.

The words "I'm fine" seem to be their mantra, but don't let that fool you. They *really* aren't okay at all. Again, let me remind you to give them room to grieve and in their own personal way. They very possibly could be in deep denial and will need some emotional help. To really feel the pain might destroy them completely, so they have isolated and buried the pain in an attempt to avoid it, or so they think. Hopefully, the day will come when they finally allow themselves to grieve their loss.

Your task then, if you are able, is to be a good listening ear and a gentle shoulder to lean on. Listen well and guide them gently, while not trying to fix them or the situation. If at this point you feel a counselor would be helpful, be honest with them and suggest it. This applies to you as well. *If you feel you need some help in your own grief, take the initiative and find it.*

Don't isolate yourself from your family and friends for very long because they will begin to worry. *Don't* let anyone rush you through your grief, but also recognize that your family and friends are there to help you move forward.

One of the things I encourage you to do is to join a Grief Support Group. Many hospitals, churches, and community organizations offer these groups. Don't let your pride convince you that you don't need it and stop you from attending. You will find people there just like you who need encouragement and support, but are perhaps at different stages of grief than you. You might even learn a thing or two, and better yet, maybe make a new friend.

I've been told that it takes five years on average to walk through the grief of losing a spouse, so you should never make any major decisions during the first years of loss. Why? Because you are still overcoming the effects of your grief and loss emotionally, physically, and spiritually, which can hinder your ability to make sound decisions. Give yourself some grace.

HELPFUL TIP 17

When you begin to experience the aftershock of grief, be patient, gentle, and kind to yourself. Minimize your expectations and extend grace to yourself and others.

CHAPTER 18

FINALIZING AFFAIRS

"The great end of life is not about knowledge, but action."

— Thomas Henry Huxley

THE GARAGE SALE

With the passing of your parent comes the clean-up and clear-out stage, and the reminiscing of days gone by. The viewing and touching of your parent's belongings may trigger memories. For many, this is sometimes where the actual grief begins. Now that the memorial or funeral is over, the condolence cards have stopped, and the medical bills have slowed down, a new journey begins. What was once a place of life and living has become a silent shadow of what used to be. The sorting and sifting feel invasive and somewhat illegal.

Going through closets and dresser drawers feels as if you are intruding on privacy and getting way too personal. After my husband's father died in late March 2013, our family was left with investments and his ten-year-old condominium. My husband, being the executor of the estate, had to begin his duties and decide what, where, and how things needed to be done. What an enormous responsibility.

The decision to have a garage sale was one of the first items on the list. My sister-in-law and her husband offered to host the event in June, so the work to sort and organize began.

I remember those first couple of times unlocking the door to the condominium and walking into the silence. Everything was still in the same place Dad had left it, but *he* was gone. It wasn't the same feeling as when I would come by to clean when he was off playing bridge or even at the hospital; nope, this was different. Here's where the reality hit. I wanted to run away to block out the emotions, but I knew it would be healthier to let them come as part of the healing process.

Let me emphasize here that crying, or what I like to call "stress leaks," are normal. Many people are embarrassed or ashamed to cry. Some have even been taught *not* to cry because it is perceived as a sign of weakness in their family. Tears are healing and medically noted as a form of ridding the body of toxins. I love to call them "stress leaks" because tears are perfectly normal and anybody can have them. No one is ever taught how to act or what to say during this phase and the hesitation and uneasiness can be foreboding.

Here are some options to consider:

1. Hire an auction company to come in and sell the home and items.
2. Contact an antique dealer that makes house calls.
3. Hire a company that does "downsizing."
4. Hire a company that does estate sales.
5. Bring your whole family in to help.
6. Simply donate it.

Depending upon your time and money, you have to determine what is the most efficient and economical way to handle the situation. Time is money for all of us. Weigh out where your energy is most needed and better used; then if you can, hire out the rest.

After walking through the condominium and assessing what needed to be done, we made plans to have a work party. Boxes were brought in many shapes and sizes, and the hours and days varied according to everyone's personal schedule. No one counted the minutes and hours we each spent; it was a collaboration of efforts, a team effort.

The condo not only held the memory of my father-in-law, but my mother-in-law as well. Mom had passed away six years before Dad, yet her memory still lingered. Items were sorted out and distributed to respective family members. Other things were sold, and some were eventually just given away. All this took time and energy, and the process created plenty of emotion, internally and externally, for everyone involved, and it was just plain hard!

CLOSING UP AFFAIRS

It took nearly three years to settle my father-in-law's estate. The garage sale was only the tip of the iceberg. With the numerous investments to sort through, piles of papers to sign, and medallion signatures needed, the process was overwhelming. In addition, we had to rent a post office box just to handle all his incoming mail.

Working with an attorney and an accountant was a wise choice. Both professionals were people my father-in-law had used in the past, so we felt more confident with their advice. We were rather shocked at how much work it would take to resolve my father-in-law's financial investments and estate. My husband and I selected to save some money and do much of the paperwork ourselves, but you need to make that decision for yourself. In case you are *not* the executor of the estate, help your family members consider their options.

Outside of the realm of finance, remember there will be names that need to be changed on titles, bank accounts, and safety deposit boxes. Social Security needs to be called, informing it of your parent's death. I encourage you to seek wise counsel with an attorney so you can do it right the first time around.

I share this information with you to prepare you, ideally in advance, because familiarizing yourself with your parent's affairs early will be of great assistance when you reach this point.

With diligence, my husband finished and closed his father's estate and affairs. The condominium was sold and distributions were made to the family. We learned a great deal through the process, especially regarding organizing *our* personal financial affairs, which we have adjusted to lighten the load for our children in the future.

HELPFUL TIP 18

Make sure you are mindful about your options and that you are making wise spending decisions. Pace yourself because the process for finalizing your parent's affairs may take a while.

CHAPTER 19

MOVING FORWARD

"Happiness is not a station you arrive at,
but a manner of traveling."

— Barbara Johnson

Moving forward after your loss can be difficult. This also takes time, just as the grief did. Again, remember that grief is a process and you may be in it for a while. You will sense the time when your grief is lessening and you are preparing to move forward.

As you begin to move forward and embrace life again, find things to do that bring you joy and a sense of being. You still have a purpose in life, but it will take time to find it. Many times, we lose ourselves while caregiving for our loved one; the things we enjoyed doing were put on hold. Now is the time to get back into those things and move forward. Remember, you are still healing from the loss, but the time has come to move on. Be cautious not to throw yourself back into life too quickly and fill your days and time with too many things or it will wear you down. Make wise choices and start small. In time, you will have more strength and stamina, but don't overdo it.

ATTENDING A SUPPORT GROUP

Attending a support group is a great way to help you heal in your walk through the process of grief, and it will help you get out of the house during the week. You will meet others walking through their own grief and loss who are looking for support just as you are. The group's support is what everyone is looking for so they have others to relate to. They will all be at different stages of their loss, but knowing others are experiencing the same thing will bring you a sense of hope. The group facilitator will have helpful information you can take home to review. Your group may also include a time for open conversation, but no one is required to speak unless he or she desires to.

VOLUNTEERING

Volunteering is a great way to get involved in life again. Numerous places are always looking for volunteers. If you have children, many schools look for extra helpers to assist in the classroom. Some of the tasks may include correcting papers, assisting with a project, doing prep work for the teacher, and assisting reading groups. The school office or library may need some extra help, so just stop in and ask.

Local food/clothing banks are another place that always need volunteers. Items constantly need sorting, packaging, and distribution.

Bake some cookies or make a meal and deliver it to someone who just came home with a new baby or just moved in across the street. Join a meal ministry at your church or in your community that delivers food to those returning home from the hospital. If a ministry you're interested in doesn't exist, start one.

If you have a pet, find out where you can take it to share a little sunshine and joy in someone's life, for example a nursing home. Be sure to ask permission in advance.

Also, hospitals need and welcome volunteers to serve at information desks and assist with discharged patients.

Hospice units always need volunteers. Many times the surviving spouse/family will deliver cookies or snacks to the kitchen area in the hospice unit for families to enjoy. They remember being in the unit with their loved one and now they want to give back.

Some volunteers are greeters and manage the front desk and sign-in area, while others sew quilts and blankets for the patients who pass through.

Volunteer at a place you would enjoy being, like the zoo or the aquarium. Your church or community can always use your help. Make it a fun adventure, not an obligation, so you look forward to it. Take it slowly and then add more hours as you decide whether it's a right fit.

JOINING A GROUP

Joining a group is another way to move forward. Getting involved with different types of groups can open the door to new adventures. A travel club/group is something you can be part of either by physically traveling or by viewing it on a big screen. I know a couple, Dave and Wendy, who travel the world and bring back beautiful pictures to be shared later with several elder groups. The elders no longer travel, but they so enjoy the sites and tutorials. What a great job Dave and Wendy are doing.

Joining a photography club, taking a college course, or joining a choir will occupy some of your time and involve you with others. You have gifts and talents, and others may want to learn from you, so go out and share yourself.

HELPFUL TIP 19

You will find your joy returning and your heart becoming lighter as you involve yourself with others and begin new things.

CHAPTER 20

LEADERSHIP

"Leadership is unlocking people's potential to become better."

— Bill Bradley

You may be wondering why I have added a chapter on leadership in my book. As a result of participating in the process of caring for a loved one, you are going to know a strength you *never* realized you had. You will then be in a unique position to help and lead other people in similar circumstances, should you choose to. What does it take to become a leader? Drive, determination, skill, and education are what most of us think of when we think of the title of leader; someone who has mastered the art of leading others.

Do pictures of strong vivacious people come to mind? Such people always become leaders, right? We are led to believe you must possess *all* of these qualities or you will never be qualified as a leader, but this is just not true.

Personally, I believe some people are natural born leaders, but many leadership skills are cultivated through education, and formal and informal training. Life is a training ground for all of us, and it is our choice to assimilate what we have learned, or throw it away. The school of hard knocks, as my father called it, offers many opportunities for learning that will continue until the day we die, so live with intention.

It was by reaching beyond the rails of my parents' hospital beds and walking through, literally, the blood, sweat, and (all the) tears, that I began to rise up and become *that* advocate, and now *that* leader.

To better serve my parents during their weakest moments in life, I felt I needed to educate myself in areas of care and advocacy I knew nothing about. I attended workshops, evening lectures, and did a lot of reading. I was *actually* hungry for information. I felt I was going through boot-camp training, but it was worth it all. I now have a wealth of knowledge and hands-on experience to share with others walking this journey. Because of this, I can lead with my personal experiences and well-earned education.

Once you have learned the skillsets in this book and have experiences under your belt from trial and error, you, too, will become a leader in this field. You might not make a career of it like I have, but you certainly will have the capacity to lead others with your own personal experiences. We all need encouragement, a helping hand, or a great word of advice during tough times. Be that person to someone else in their time of need. Give them a copy of this book and tell them to read the chapters that were most helpful to you. Don't be afraid to help, lead, and guide them through some of their own challenges. *That* is what leadership is; it begins by leading one person at a time.

Throughout my life, I have always enjoyed volunteer work. It gives me purpose in life and always benefits others, which brings joy to my heart. For the past twelve years, I have been volunteering at my church, Shoreline Community Church, as the care team leader. The team consists of both men and women, and we all vary in age and skill levels. Our mission is to reach and touch those in our church and surrounding community who need personal contact or care. By extending the hand of care, we can make a difference. With encouraging words and moral support, we reach out with cards, phone calls, visitations, temporary meal deliveries, and occasional transportation. The team travels to private homes, hospitals, adult family homes, nursing care facilities, and memory care units—anywhere we are needed. What a great team of people I am privileged to lead!

Early in my new role as care team leader, I began to sense a larger need stirring not just in our congregation, but in our community. A great need existed for tangible information to help those caring for an ill parent/loved one. The "silver tsunami" had just begun. This was the first term I had heard for the Baby Boomer generation's great migration into retirement. With this massive shift in society comes the need for more retirement living space, assisted living facilities, etc., and of course, more in-home care workers. Communities are feeling this great shift and have to adjust to the increase in need. This has also been called the "sandwich generation," which means the primary caregiver for an elderly parent still has young children at home to raise. These caregivers are literally caring for both simultaneously; hence, they are sandwiched in.

This situation is extremely exhausting, I know, because I have personally experienced it. With this growing change in my own community, I began pondering the idea of a seminar to educate and encourage people in this position. Alzheimer's disease was on the rise and people wanted to learn more. With no instruction manual on how to care for their aging parent or an ill loved one, people were at a loss what to do, and they needed some help. With that need in mind, I created the first Shoreline Community Church Care Conference.

What began as a one-day event, the following years grew into a two-day, ten-hour event with close to 300 attendees. It was a free event with a boxed lunch, and everyone was welcomed. We were fortunate to secure Teepa Snow (as discussed in Chapter 5), a nationally recognized dementia care consultant and expert, three years in a row as our keynote speaker. It was there I unveiled my first book, *My Personal Health Care Notebook* (which is now *The Personal Health Care Manual*). I was so passionate about people owning one of my manuals that each attendee received a free copy at our events.

I lectured on the content and importance of using the manual as a voice for their loved one when their loved one no longer had a voice of their own. I relayed information about my personal journey with my ill parents, and I spoke about some of the obstacles and challenges that got in the way. I shared skills to overcome these obstacles and challenges to navigate through complex issues. My goal was to meet people wherever they were on their journey to offer help and education (and a little bit of love).

All three Care Conferences were well-attended and a huge success. Even now, people are asking when the next Care Conference will be scheduled. As I pen these words, arrangements are being made for the next Care Conference in March 2019 in Shoreline, Washington. I can't wait; it will be awesome! My hope is to see more and more of these types of events happening in communities all across America and to be one of many expert speakers on this topic.

One thing I bring to the table that others may not is that I'm not afraid to begin the hard conversations, but I also make it a point to reach across the table to truly touch the lives of others and offer the personal connection desperately needed by *all* during the journey of care.

So here is the challenge: What have you learned or walked through that could help, encourage, or even inspire someone else? Think about it and then take that step forward. You are a leader whether you realize it or not.

HELPFUL TIP 20

Once your knowledge base has grown and you have learned new tools, you never go back to your initial state of not-knowing. This puts you in the unique position to lead others who are going through the same things you have experienced. Walk tall and lend a hand and heart whenever possible. Remember the fear, bewilderment, and sadness you experienced when you began this process, and share your experience, strength, and hope with others. You are a leader and you have much to give. Teach those around you how to treat their parents with *respect, honor, and dignity.*

A FINAL NOTE

Now that you have read this book, what are *you* going to do? It's time to take action. You have been given many tools, so let's put them to use. I challenge you to take the first step in your Action Plan now by going to my website to purchase *The Personal Health Care Manual*, which will help you begin your journey. It will really help organize your parents' health information in a practical and effective order. Take action!

Next, I am encouraging you to use the space below to begin the second step of your Action Plan. List nine additional actions you will take in the next thirty days as a result of reading my book.

1. Order a copy of *The Personal Health Care Manual* for Mom/Dad
2. ____
3. ____
4. ____
5. ____

6. ____

7. ____

8. ____

9. ____

10. ____

In this book, you have learned dozens of tips, tools, and strategies to help you on your journey. Most importantly, you have learned how to prioritize your parent above all else by treating them with the *respect, honor, and dignity* they deserve until the very end. Margery Williams, author of *The Velveteen Rabbit*, captured the heart and soul of what I have come to believe when she wrote:

"Hearts acquire greater humanity through pain and adversity... that life is a process of constant change—there are departures for some and arrivals for others—and the process allows us to grow and persevere."

I wish you all the best on your journey with your loved one, be it your mother, father, brother, sister, husband, wife, or even your child. When we dare to love someone, we run the risk of being loved in return. I am here to encourage you, and I am praying for you. Be strong and take courage....

With Joy,

Sue Stults

Sue Stults

ABOUT THE AUTHOR

The catalyst for Sue Stults to become an advocate for those needing end-of-life care and their caregivers was when she walked with her father through terminal lung cancer, an incredibly difficult experience that stretched every part of her being. After that journey, her vision for patient care, advocacy, and family support began forming into something greater. Finally, in 2012, Compelled by Compassion, Inc. was born.

However, many years earlier, her skills for advocating and caring for people had begun to develop. A cosmetologist by trade, Sue seemed to find herself speaking hope and reconciliation into her clients' lives as they frequently poured out to her stories of frustration and struggle while they sat in her chair during routine hair appointments.

Beyond that, during the time she and her husband raised their four children, Sue was constantly involved in coordinating volunteers for events, as well as advocating and supporting a variety of community groups. Through these experiences, she found herself in a position of caring and advocating for those around her.

After her father passed away in 1999, Sue continued to navigate the health care system as she walked through health complications with her mother, both of her husbands' parents, and many others near and dear to her. Together, they journeyed through the confusion and frustration of the health care system.

As a result, Sue became very involved in patient care and advocacy. She acquired new skills and incredible bits of information that were compiled to create her first book and the centerpiece of her business, *The Personal Health Care Manual.* This manual is an assortment of hand-selected documents that everyone should take the time to complete. It includes medication lists, doctor contact information, emergency contacts, directives, hospice information, and much more. It is designed for individual use and is a great tool for professionals and family.

It is Sue's hope that *The Personal Health Care Manual* will serve as a companion to this book to help you organize essential health care information for yourself and your parent or loved one, easing your load and providing you with some direction and peace of mind as you walk this difficult road.

Sue Stults is an engaging author, keynote speaker, personal health care advisor, and chaplain. She has been working in the senior industry for almost twenty years, and she is the founder of Compelled by Compassion, Inc. located in the Greater Seattle area.

Sue helps families navigate through the confusion and frustration of caring for an aging parent. Through workshops, seminars, and Care Conferences, Sue focuses on the principles of *respect, honor, and dignity*. Sue encourages and empowers families to be *the* advocate and a voice for those who no longer have one. With her tender heart and personal insights, Sue comes alongside and coaches people through the *blood, sweat, and tears of caring for Mom and Dad.*

CONSIDER HIRING SUE STULTS AS YOUR ADVISOR

Consider hiring Sue Stults, Founder and President of Compelled by Compassion, Inc., to be your advisor and coach as you walk through the journey of caring for your parent or a loved one. She has the tools to lead and guide you, and she will encourage you each step along the way. Sue is a great sounding board and an intentional listener. Let her help you find solutions and answers.

Contact Sue today to schedule your thirty-minute complimentary consultation:

www.SueStults.com

(425) 770-2775

BOOK SUE STULTS TO SPEAK AT YOUR NEXT EVENT

Sue's twenty years of experience, dedication, and service in the care of Seniors has granted her the expertise and knowledge to help you navigate *the road of care* for you and your loved one. Sue has firsthand experience from caring for her parents and leading community conferences on caring for the ill and aging. She will craft and present her information in a gentle, concise, and at times, humorous fashion. She is sure to tug at your heartstrings as you gain knowledge and insight. Sue is not afraid to speak about the tough issues around death and dying because she knows someone has to. She facilitates the conversation while empowering her audiences. Invite Sue to be *your* next speaker. Contact her at:

www.SueStults.com

www.ReachingBeyondTheRail.com

(425) 770-2775